Introduction

Science is about asking questions. Physics is the science that asks questions about the physical world around you, its practical uses, and some of the social issues it raises.

You will find this book useful if you are studying physics as part of a Single or Double Award GCSE science course.

Everything in this book has been organized to help you find out things quickly and easily. It is written in two-page units called spreads.

Use the contents page

If you are looking for information on a large topic, look it up in the contents page.

Use the index

If there is something small you want to check on, look up the most likely word in the index. The index gives the page number where you'll find information about that word.

Use the questions

Asking questions and answering them is a very good way of learning. There are questions at the end of every chapter. At the end of the book there is a set of further exam-style questions. Answers to numerical questions, and some pointers to those requiring short answers are provided.

Use the key words glossary

At the end of each chapter there are a selection of key words and their meanings to help you understand the main ideas given in the chapter.

Helping you revise

To help you revise, in addition to the questions, and the end-of-chapter glossaries of important terms, there are some revision notes, and some further exam-style questions.

Physics is an important and exciting subject. It doesn't just happen in laboratories. It is all around you: in fairgrounds, fields, farms, and factories. It is taking place deep in the Earth and far out in space. You'll find physics everywhere.

I hope that this book helps you with your studies, that you enjoy using it, and that at the end of your course, you agree with me!

Stephen Pople
July 2001

Physics

Contents

Note: Spreads 3.10, 3.11, 3.12 are included to satisfy the requirements of particular specifications. Check they are required by the one you are studying.

Written for the NEW Specifications

Target Science

Physics
Foundation Tier

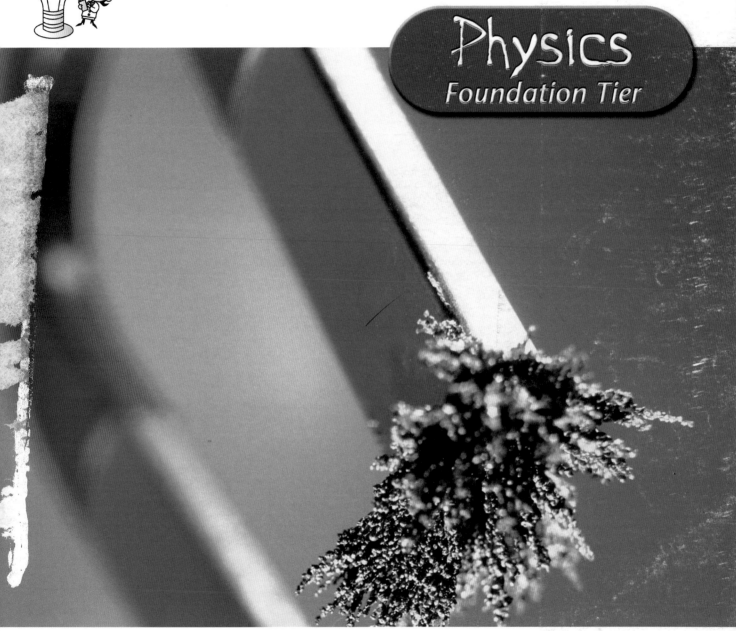

Stephen Pople

OXFORD
UNIVERSITY PRESS

OXFORD

UNIVERSITY PRESS

Great Clarendon Street, Oxford OX2 6DP

Oxford University Press is a department of the University of Oxford.
It furthers the University's objective of excellence in research, scholarship,
and education by publishing worldwide in

Oxford New York

Athens Auckland Bangkok Bogotá Buenos Aires Cape Town
Chennai Dar es Salaam Delhi Florence Hong Kong Istanbul Karachi
Kolkata Kuala Lumpur Madrid Melbourne Mexico City Mumbai Nairobi
Paris São Paulo Shanghai Singapore Taipei Tokyo Toronto Warsaw
with associated companies in Berlin Ibadan

British Library Cataloguing in Publication Data

Data available

ISBN 0-19-914828-7

Typeset in Stone Serif
by Ian Foulis & Associates, Plymouth UK
Printed by
Butler & Tanner Ltd, Frome UK

Acknowledgements

(Leslie Garland Picture Library = LGPL, Robert Harding Picture Library = RGPL, Science Photo Library = SPL; l = left, r = right, t = top, c = centre, b = bottom.)

7 © G. Houser/Corbis; 11l Philip Mould, Historical Portraits Ltd, London UK/Bridgeman Art Library; 11r Frank Zullo/SPL; 12 Russell Cheyne/Allsport; 17 SPL; 18 Getty Images Stone; 19r Collections/Brian Shuel; 21 Andrew Lambert/Leslie Garland; 23 Image Bank; 22 Charles Winters/SPL; 24 Amy Trustram/SPL; 28 © Kevin R. Morris/Corbis; 30 Wattie Cheung/Camera Press; 34r © Jack Hollingsworth/Corbis; 34l © Roy Morsch/The Stockmarket; 36 Leslie Garland; 40 Will & Deni McIntyre/SPL; 41 www.shoutpictures.com; 42 Mark Wagner/Flight Collection; 43 Epson; 44c RGPL; 44t © Tom Ives/The Stockmarket; 45bl www.shoutpictures.com; 45br SPL; 45cl www.shoutpictures.com; 45tr www.shoutpictures.com; 46b Aircare; 46t Image Bank; 47 Peter Menzel/SPL; 53 © Paul A. Souders/Corbis; 54 Michael Steele/Allsport; 55 NASA; 56 l Flight Collection; 56 r © David Lawrence/The Stockmarket; 63 tr Alvey & Towers Picture Library; 63b Chris Cole/Allsport; 63tl Takeshi Takahara/SPL; 64t www.shoutpictures.com; 65 Getty Images Stone; 66 Getty Images Stone; 69b Auto Express; 69t Auto Express; 73 © Duomo/Corbis; 74 Superstock; 75 Jeremy Walker/SPL; 76 Corel; 78b Tony Duffy/Allsport; 78t John Welzenbach/ The Stockmarket; 79b Clive Brunskill/Allsport; 79t Allsport; 80bl © Chris van Lennep, Gallo Images/Corbis; 80r © Richard Hamilton Smith/Corbis; 80tl FPG/Telegraph Colour Library; 87 © Michael & Patricia Fogden/Corbis; 88 Pete Turner/Image Bank; 91 Andrew Lambert/LGPL; 92 Getty Images Stone; 93t © Chris Rogers/The Stockmarket; 93b Auto Express; 94 © Philip James Corwin/Corbis; 96 Andrew Lambert/LPGL; 97 © Raymond Gehman/Corbis; 99l Superstock; 99r Dr K. Schiller/SPL; 100c Adam-Hart Davis/SPL; 100b © William Taufic/The Stockmarket; 103 Alfred Pasieka/SPL; 106 Keith Kent/SPL; 108l © David Lees/Corbis; 108r © Neal Preston/Corbis; 109 © Moshe Shai/Corbis; 110 N. N. Birks/Ardea; 111 © Yoav Levy/Phototake/RGPL; 112 © Roger Ressmeyer/Corbis; 115 © Jim Sugar Photography/Corbis; 116 © Roger Ressmeyer/Corbis; 118b © Jan Butchofsky-Houser/Corbis; 118c © David H. Wells/Corbis; 118t © Paul A Souders/Corbis; 119 © Henry Diltz/Corbis; 120b Lester Lefkowitz/The Stockmarket; 120t Luis F. Rodriguez; 121r G. & M. David de Lossy/ Image Bank; 127 NASA; 129t SPL; 132br SPL; 132br L. Pesek/SPL; 132t NASA/SPL; 134tl SPL; 134bl STScI/NASA; 134br Ken M. Johns/SPL; 134tr European Space Agency/SPL; 137 Tony Hallas/SPL; 138 NASA; 139 NASA; 140b David Parker/SPL; 140t Getty Images Stone; 142 © Jonathan Blair/Corbis; 142b Photodisc; 142c NASA; 142t Photodisc; 147 © Charles & Josette Lenars/Corbis; 148 Superstock; 152 © Bob Winsett/Corbis; 153 © Tim McKenna/The Stockmarket; 155 © Frans Lanting/Minden Pictures/RGPL; 156 Getty Images Stone; 158 © Michael Kevin Daly/The Stockmarket; 160 © Patrick Ward/Corbis; 161 Rosenfeld Images Ltd/SPL; 162b Getty Images Stone; 162l Adam Hart-Davis/SPL; 164 © Bryan F. Teyerson/The Stockmarket; 165 Lowell Georgia/SPL; 169 Edifice; 170b © The Purcell Team/Corbis; 170tl © Layne Kennedy/Corbis; 170tr © Raissa Page/Format; 171b Corel Professional Photos; 171c © John Marshall Mantel/Corbis; 171t Allsport/UK Allsport; 177 Corel Professional Photos; 179b © Yoav Levy/Phototake/RGPL; 179t SPL; 182 Jeremy Walker/SPL; 182b Alvey & Towers Picture Library; 182r Alvey & Towers Picture Library; 185 Andrew Lambert/LGPL; 189 Getty Images Stone; 191b Andrew Lambert/LGPL; 191t Alvey & Towers Picture Library; 192 US Dept of Energy/SPL; 193 © WildCountry/Corbis; 194b LondonWaste Ltd; 194c SPL; 194l Martin Bond/SPL; 194t Holt Studios International; 195 Edison Mission Energy; 196b Martin Bond/SPL; 196t RGPL; 197 Hulton Getty; 201 Photodisc; 205 S. Morgan/Frank Spooner; 206t Rex Features; 206l Klaus Guldbrandsen/SPL; 210 © Yoav Levy/Phototake/RGPL; 211 © Werner Forman/Corbis; 212 SPL; 213l Mere Words/SPL; 213r UKAEA.

Any uncredited images are from the OUP archive, Peter Gould, or Andrew Lambert.

The publisher wishes to acknowledge the help of Brian Arnold in the preparation of the questions.

Routemaps

The order of content provided by a Specification does not always suit all students. There is no one right way through a Specification. These *Routemaps* offer alternative pathways through topics and have been constructed to help you 'understand' concepts in small, logical sections. They are particularly useful when revising as they help you identify and revise small sections at a time. They are also useful to use to catch up if for any reason you have missed any work.

ELECTRICITY

Currents and circuits
2.01 – 2.07
2.09

Charge and its effects
2.12 – 2.13

Mains electricity
2.08
2.10 – 2.11

FORCES AND MOTION

Motion
3.01 – 3.03

Effects of forces
3.04 – 3.07
3.09 – 3.12

Speed and safety
3.08

ENERGY

Energy transfer
6.04 – 6.05

Work, energy and power
6.01 – 6.03
6.06

Supplying energy
6.07 – 6.10

THE EARTH IN SPACE

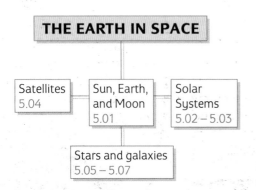

Satellites
5.04

Sun, Earth, and Moon
5.01

Solar Systems
5.02 – 5.03

Stars and galaxies
5.05 – 5.07

CURRENTS AND MAGNETS

Magnetic fields
7.01

Electric motors
7.04 – 7.05

Fields from currents
7.02 – 7.03

Generators and transformers
7.06 – 7.07

Power across the country
7.08

ATOMS AND NUCLEI

Inside atoms
8.01

Nuclear radiation
8.02 – 8.03

Using radiation
8.05

Radioactive decay
8.04

RAYS AND WAVES

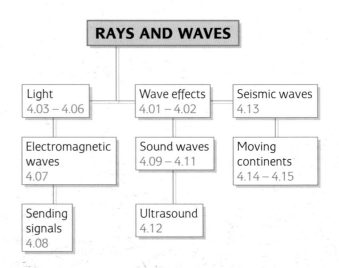

Light
4.03 – 4.06

Wave effects
4.01 – 4.02

Seismic waves
4.13

Electromagnetic waves
4.07

Sound waves
4.09 – 4.11

Moving continents
4.14 – 4.15

Sending signals
4.08

Ultrasound
4.12

Units and measurements 1

This astronomical clock doesn't only tell the time. It also shows the positions of the Sun and Moon relative to the stars in the night sky. Until about fifty years ago, scientists had to rely on mechanical clocks, such as the one above, to measure time. Today, they can use atomic clocks whose timekeeping varies by less than a second in a million years.

A system of units

Objectives

This spread should help you to
- give the SI units of mass, length, and time
- say what kilo, milli, and micro mean

mass

time

length

*You can measure the mass of a small object using a **balance** like this one.*

Questions

1 What is the SI unit of mass?
2 What is the SI unit of length?
3 What is the SI unit of time?
4 What do the following stand for?

kilo   milli   micro

5 Which is the greater:

a 1600 g or 1.5 kg?
b 1250 mm or 1.3 m?

People measure things using many different units, including those shown above. But in scientific work, life is much easier if everyone uses a common system of units.

Most scientists use **SI units** (full name: Système International d'Unités). This system starts with the kilogram, metre, and second – for measuring mass, length, and time. From these come a whole range of units for measuring volume, speed, force, energy, and other quantities.

On the opposite page, there is more information about the kilogram, metre, and second, and bigger and smaller units based on them.

Bigger and smaller

You can make a unit bigger or smaller by putting an extra symbol, called a **prefix**, in front (in the chart below, W stands for **watt**, the SI unit of power):

Prefix	Meaning	Example
M (mega)	× 1 000 000	MW (megawatt)
k (kilo)	× 1000	km (kilometre)
d (deci)	$\times \frac{1}{10}$	dm (decimetre)
c (centi)	$\times \frac{1}{100}$	cm (centimetre)
m (milli)	$\times \frac{1}{1000}$	mm (millimetre)
μ (micro)	$\times \frac{1}{1000000}$	μW (microwatt)

Note: milli means 'thousandth', not millionth; micro means 'millionth'.

Mass Mass is the amount of matter in something.
The SI unit of mass is the **kilogram** (symbol kg).
You can measure the mass of a small object using a **balance**
like the one in the photograph on the opposite page.

milligram (mg)   gram (g)   kilogram (kg)   tonne (t)

hair

bank note

1000 mg = 1 g   1000 g = 1 kg   1 t = 1000 kg

Length The SI unit of length is the **metre** (symbol m).

micrometre (μm)   millimetre (mm)   centimetre (cm)   metre (m)   kilometre (km)

living cells

1000 000 μm = 1 m   1000 mm = 1 m   100 cm = 1 m   1 km = 1000 m

Time The SI unit of time is the **second** (symbol s).
For shorter times, the **millisecond** (symbol ms) is
sometimes used: 1000 ms = 1 s

Questions

6 Copy and complete this table:

	Unit	Symbol
Length	?	m
?	kilogram	?
Time	?	?

7 What do the following stand for?

g   mm   mg   t   ms   μm

8 10   100   1000   100 000   1000 000
Which of the above is:
a the number of mg in 1 g?
b the number of mm in 1 cm?
c the number of cm in 1 m?
d the number of cm in 1 km?
e the number of mm in 1 km?

9 Write down the value of:
a 1 m in mm.   **b** 1.5 m in mm.
c 1.534 m in mm.   **d** 1652 mm in m.

10 Write down the value of:
a 1 kg in g.   **b** 1750 g in kg.
c 26 t in kg.   **d** 6 s in ms.

More about units

Objectives

This spread should help you to

- give the units of volume
- explain what density means

Volume

Volume is the amount of space that something takes up.

The SI unit of volume is the **cubic metre** (m³). This is rather a large unit for everyday use, so smaller units based on it are often used instead.

Cubic metre (m³)

1 cubic metre (m³) = 1000 litres (l)

1 m   1 m   1 m

1 cubic metre (m³) is the volume of a cube measuring 1 m × 1 m × 1 m.

Litre (l or L)

Note: the symbol for litre can be confused with a 1 (one).

1 litre (l) = 1000 cubic centimetres (cm³)

= 1000 millilitres (ml)

1 litre is the same volume as 1 cubic decimetre (dm³).

Cubic centimetre (cm³) or millilitre (ml or ML)

1 cubic centimetre (cm³) is the volume of a cube measuring 1 cm × 1 cm × 1 cm. It is the same volume as 1 millilitre (ml).

Density

New units can be made by combining others together. **Density** is one example:

Water has a density of 1000 kilograms per cubic metre (kg/m³). This means that each cubic metre of water has a mass of 1000 kilograms. The densities of some other materials are given in the chart below.

People may say that 'lead is heavier than water'. But that isn't necessarily true. A small piece of lead is lighter than a bucketful of water! However, lead is more *dense* than water because it has more kilograms packed into every cubic metre.

Examples of density values are shown below. The density of air can vary a lot, depending on how compressed the air is.

1.3 kg/m³	750 kg/m³	800 kg/m³	1000 kg/m³
air	**wood**	**petrol**	**water**

2700 kg/m³	7800 kg/m³	11 300 kg/m³	19 300 kg/m³
aluminium	**steel**	**lead**	**gold**

The least dense material you are ever likely to see is the dimly glowing gas in the tail of a comet (right). Millions of kilometres long, the gas is so thin that there is less than a kilogram per cubic kilometre.

*The densest substance found on Earth is the rare metal **osmium**. It is about twice as dense as lead. If this book were made of osmium, it would weigh as much as a full bucket of water.*

Sir Isaac Newton (1642–1727). The unit of force was named after him.

Names and symbols

Units like the metre, kilogram, and second are always written in 'small' letters, without capitals. So are their symbols (the abbreviations, or 'short' versions):

Unit	Symbol (abbreviation)	Measures...
metre	m	length
kilogram	kg	mass
second	s	time

Some units are named after famous scientists – such as Isaac Newton, Blaise Pascal, and André Ampère:

Unit	Symbol (abbreviation)	Measures...
newton	N	force
pascal	Pa	pressure
ampere	A	current

When a person's name is used as a unit, it is *not* written with a capital letter at the start. However, the symbol *does* have a capital.

Questions

1 A bottle of cola has a volume of 2 litres. What is its volume:
a in cm^3? **b** in ml?

2 The density of aluminium is 2700 kg/m^3. What is the mass of:
a 1 m^3 of aluminium?
b 10 m^3 of aluminium?

3 Use information from the chart of densities on the opposite page to help you answer the following:
a Which has more mass, 1 m^3 of petrol or 1 m^3 of water?
b Which has more volume (takes up most space), 1 kg of petrol or 1 kg of water?

Over the centuries, people have used a wide variety of units for making measurements. Here are some examples.

STRANGE *but true!*

The **foot** (unit of length) was originally the length of a Roman's foot. But some people had much longer feet than others! So, in the 12th century the foot was defined by a law issued by Henry I of England as the total width of 36 ears of barleycorn.

The **acre** (unit of area) was the area of a field that could be ploughed in one day by a team of two oxen.

The **knot** (unit of speed) is still used by mariners at sea and by pilots. It is 1.15 m.p.h., or about 0.5 metres per second. Speed at sea was originally measured by letting a knotted rope out behind the boat and seeing how many knots floated away from the ship in a set time.

The **hand** (unit of length) is the width of an average hand. It is still used for measuring the height of horses.

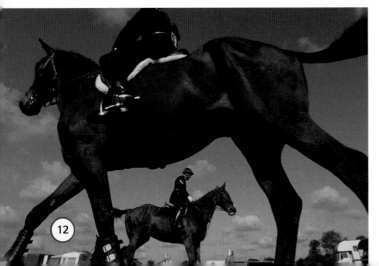

12 inches = 1 foot
3 feet = 1 yard
22 yards = 1 chain
10 chains = 1 furlong
8 furlongs = 1 mile

Most scientists now use units based on the metric system. This was introduced by French scientists in the 1790s, after the French Revolution. It sorted out the muddled systems of units used before by basing everything on the number 10.

10 millimetres = 1 centimetre
100 centimetres = 1 metre
1000 metres = 1 kilometre

The **metre** (unit of length) was defined as one forty millionth of the Earth's circumference. The standard metre was a bar with two marks on it, kept in Paris.

The **gram** (unit of mass) was defined as the mass of one cubic centimetre of water.

The original definitions of the metric system are not accurate enough for modern scientific work. For example, a 'standard' metre bar will expand and contract slightly if its temperature varies, so it isn't really standard at all! That is why scientists have had to come up with new and better ways of defining units. Here, for example, is the modern definition of the metre:

LASER

1 metre

The metre is the distance travelled by light in a vacuum in a time of

$$\frac{1}{299\,792\,458} \text{ seconds.}$$

Of course, to define the metre like this, you have to have an exact definition of the second, and that is complicated. It is based on the rate of a vibration which can occur in a certain type of caesium atom.

Talking points

Scientists use SI units, based on the metric system. For example, the metre is a unit. The *quantity* it measures is length.

Look up the following units in the index in this book. Find out what quantity each one measures:

newton   joule   ohm   ampere   watt

1 Copy and complete the table shown below.

Measurement	Unit	Symbol
Length	?	?
Mass	?	?
?	?	s
?	Ampere	?
Temperature	?	?
Area	—	?
?	—	m³
?	Newton	?

2 **a** How many mg are there in 1 g?

   b How many g are there in 1 kg?

   c How many mg are there in 1 kg?

   d How many mm are there in 4 km?

   e How many cm are there in 5 km?

3 Write down the values of:

   a 300 cm in   m

   b 500 g in   kg

   c 1500 m in   km

   d 250 ms in   s

   e 0.5 s in   ms

   f 0.75km in   m

   g 2.5 kg in   g

   h 0.8 m in   mm

4 Copy and complete the table shown below.

Length	Width	Height	Volume of rectangular block
2 cm	3 cm	4 cm	?
5 cm	5 cm	?	100 cm³
6 cm	?	5 cm	300 cm³
?	10 cm	10 cm	500 cm³

5 Calculate the density of the following:

   a a piece of steel which has a volume of 6 cm³ and a mass of 48g.

   b a piece of copper which has a volume of 10 cm³ and a mass of 90 g.

   c a piece of gold which has a volume of 2.0 cm³ and a mass of 38 g.

6 Calculate the mass of the following:

   a 4 cm³ of aluminium. The density of aluminium is 2.7 g/cm³.

   b 20 cm³ of wood. The density of wood is 0.80 g/cm³.

   c 80 cm³ of glass. The density of glass is 2.5 g/cm³.

7 Calculate the volume of the following:

   a 68 g of mercury. The density of mercury is 13.6 g/cm³.

   b 15.8 g of iron. The density of iron is 7.9 g/cm³.

   c 99 g of lead. The density of lead is 11 g/cm³.

Key words

The spread numbers in brackets tell you where to find more information.

density If a material with a mass of 1000 kg has a volume of 1 cubic metre, then its density is 1000 kg/m^3. *(1.02, 4.13)*

kilogram (kg) Unit of mass. *(1.01)*

mass The amount of matter in something. It is measured in kilograms (kg). *(1.01)*

metre (m) Unit of length. 1000 metres equals 1 kilometre (km). *(1.01)*

second (s) Unit of time. *(1.01)*

volume The amount of space something takes up. It is measured in cubic metres (m^3). A smaller unit of volume is the cubic centimetre (cm^3), or millilitre (ml). 1 cm^3 = 1 ml = 1/1 000 000 m^3. *(1.02)*

A worker inside a safety cage looks on as 2.5 million volt sparks come from a huge Van de Graaff generator. The sparks are produced when electric charge flows through the air, heats it, and makes it light up. Heating and lighting are just two of electricity's effects, although the results are usually less spectacular than this experiment.

Electricity on the move

When you switch on a hairdrier, lamp, or TV, the 'electricity' in the wires is a flow of tiny particles called **electrons**. These are so small that they can pass between the atoms of the wire. They each carry a tiny electric **charge**.

A flow of charge is called a **current**. So a flow of electrons is a current.

When a torch is working, more than 1 million million million electrons flow through its bulb every second!

Conductors and insulators

Materials that let current pass through are called **conductors**. Materials that do not let current pass through are **insulators**. Here are some examples.

Conductors		Insulators	
Good	*Poor*	plastics	glass
metals	human body	*for example*	rubber
especially	water	PVC	
silver	air	polythene	
copper		Perspex	
aluminium			
carbon			

In an electric cable like the one on the left, copper wires carry the current. The PVC insulation stops current flowing between the wires, and stops the wires touching anything outside the cable.

Questions

1 What word means:

a a flow of charge?

b a material that lets current pass through?

c a material that does not let current pass through?

PVC (insulator)

copper (conductor)

The bulbs on this carnival float get their current from a generator turned by a diesel engine.

A cell.

Sources of current

Our main sources of current are electric **cells**, **batteries**, and **generators**. For example, mains current comes from huge generators in power stations.

Cells and batteries push out current when chemicals inside them react. Generators push out current when a shaft is turned. In power stations, the generators are often turned by turbines driven round by jets of high-pressure steam from a boiler.

Using current

A current is a convenient way of delivering energy. Here are some of the ways of using that energy:

source of current

heat   light   sound   motion

Questions

2 Name a material that could be used for making each of the following:

  a the wire inside an electric cable.

  b the insulation round the outside of the cable.

3 Write down the name of a device which:

  a pushes out a current when chemicals react inside it.

  b pushes out a current when a shaft is turned.

4 Write down:

  a two things that get their current from cells or batteries.

  b two things that get their current from generators.

5 Write down:

  a two things that use current to produce motion.

  b two things that use current to produce heat.

  c two things that use current to produce sound.

Circuits and currents

Objectives

This spread should help you to
- describe what a circuit is
- explain how current is measured

A simple circuit

Below, a **cell** has been connected to a bulb and a switch. The complete loop is known as a **circuit**. Electrons are pushed out of the **negative (–) terminal** of the cell, through the bulb and switch, and round to the **positive (+) terminal**. As they pass through the bulb, they heat up a tiny filament (thin wire) so that it glows.

There must be a *complete* circuit for electrons to flow. If there is a break in the circuit, the flow stops, and the bulb goes out. Turning the switch OFF breaks the circuit.

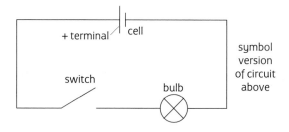

Circuit symbols

To keep things easy, scientists and electricians draw circuits using special symbols. You can see an example above.

Unfortunately, the standard symbol for a switch looks OFF even though the switch may be ON! So alternative symbols are sometimes used. There is also an alternative symbol for a bulb.

Questions

1 Give *two* things that are necessary to make a current flow through a small bulb.

2 What do the following symbols mean?

a   b   c

An ammeter in use.

ammeter symbol

Measuring current

Current is measured in **amperes** (A). The higher the current, the greater the flow of charge. In other words, the more electrons pass round the circuit every second.

To measure current, you connect an **ammeter** into the circuit, as shown in the examples below. Fitting the ammeter doesn't affect the current. As far as the circuit is concerned, the ammeter is just like another piece of connecting wire.

 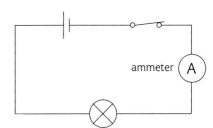

In simple circuits like those above, it doesn't matter where the ammeter goes, because the current is the same all the way round. The same electrons pass through one section after another.

Small currents can be measured in **milliamperes** (mA):

$$1000\,\text{mA} = 1\,\text{A}$$

So, for example, a current of 0.4 A is 400 mA.

Current direction

On some circuit diagrams, you may see an arrowhead. This is called the **conventional current direction**. It isn't really a direction of flow. It just shows the direction from positive (+) to negative (–) round the circuit. The electrons actually flow the opposite way.

Questions

3   In the circuit on the right, meters X and Y measure current.

   a   What type of meter are X and Y?

   b   Would you expect the reading on meter Y to be *more*, *less*, or the *same* as that on meter X?

  If the switch is opened...

   c   will bulb A stay on or go out?

   d   will bulb B stay on or go out?

   e   what will happen to the reading on meter X?

   f   what will happen to the reading on meter Y?

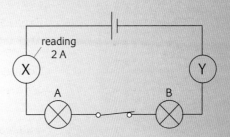

4   The current through a small torch bulb is 0.2 A. What is this in milliamperes?

Voltage

Cells store energy. When a cell is connected into a circuit, as below, chemical reactions inside the cell push out electrons and *give* them energy. The electrons *lose* this energy when they flow through the bulb. The energy is given off as heat and light.

cell gives
electrons energy

electrons return to cell

electrons carry energy to bulb

electrons lose energy
energy given off as heat and light

Did you know?

Typical voltages

Voltage across...

... a cell for a torch	1.5 V
... a car battery	12 V
... a mains socket	230 V

Cells and voltage

Cells have a **voltage** marked on the side. The higher the voltage, the more energy each electron is given.

Voltage is also known as **potential difference** (**p.d.**). It is measured in **volts** (V). The voltage of a cell can be measured by connecting a **voltmeter** across its terminals.

reading 1.5 V

voltmeter

cell

reading 3.0 V

voltmeter

two cells in series

If two identical cells are connected in **series** (in a line), the total voltage across them is twice that across a single cell.

A collection of linked cells is called a **battery**, although the word is commonly used for a single cell as well.

This 12 volt car battery has six 2 volt cells connected in series, all in the same case.

symbols

voltmeter

battery
(2 cells)

battery
(several cells)

Questions

1 How would you draw three cells in series, using symbols?

2 What type of meter would you use to measure p.d.?

3 What single word means the same thing as p.d.?

Voltages round a circuit

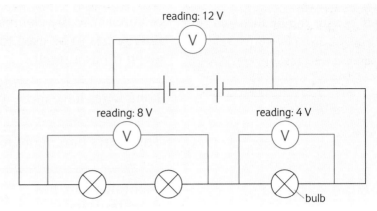

reading: 12 V

reading: 8 V

reading: 4 V

bulb

Most personal CD players are powered by two 1.5 V cells connected in series.

Above, a 12 V battery has been connected across three bulbs. The electrons lose some of their energy in the first bulb, some in the second, and the rest in the third.

Connect a voltmeter across any of the bulbs and it shows a reading. The higher the voltage, the more energy each electron loses as it passes through that part of the circuit.

Between them, the bulbs give out all the energy supplied by the battery:

The voltages across the bulbs add up to equal the battery voltage.

Connecting the voltmeters has no effect on the current flowing in the circuit above. As far as the circuit is concerned, the voltmeters might as well not be there.

Questions

4 The circuit on the right contains a battery and two bulbs.

  a Which part of the circuit stores energy?

  b In which parts of the circuit is energy being used?

  c The battery is made up of three cells. What would you expect the voltage of each cell to be?

  d What will be the reading on meter **Z**?

  e If an extra cell is added to the battery, what would you expect the new reading to be on...

  meter **X**?   meter **Y**?   meter **Z**?

5 Look at the circuit at the top of this page. If the meter that reads 8 V was connected across only one bulb instead of two, what would you expect it to read?

reading: 6 V

X

reading: 3 V

Y

Z

Resistance

Objectives

This spread should help you to

- calculate resistance
- explain what resistors are

Current passes easily through a piece of copper connecting wire. It doesn't pass so easily through the thin nichrome wire of an electric fire element. The wire has more **resistance**. Energy has to be used to force electrons through it, and heat is given off as a result.

Long wires have more resistance...   ... than short ones.

Thin wires have more resistance...   ... than thick ones.

Nichrome wire has more resistance...   ... than copper wire of the same size.

Calculating resistance

Resistance is measured in **ohms** (Ω). If a voltage is put across the ends of a wire, a current flows. The resistance of the wire, in ohms, can be calculated using this equation:

$$\text{resistance} = \frac{\text{voltage}}{\text{current}}$$

voltage in volts (V)
current in amperes (A)
resistance in ohms (Ω)

For example:

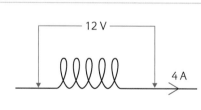

If there is a voltage of 12 V across this piece of nichrome wire, a current of 4 A flows. So:

$$\text{resistance} = \frac{12}{4} = 3\,\Omega$$

If there is a voltage of 12 V across this piece of nichrome wire, a current of 2 A flows. So:

$$\text{resistance} = \frac{12}{2} = 6\,\Omega$$

So, for any particular voltage:

The *higher* the resistance, the *lower* the current through the wire.

Heat from resistance

When current flows through a resistance, heat is given off. This idea is used in the filament of a light bulb. It is also used in the heating elements of electric kettles, irons, toasters, and hairdriers.

Questions

1 In what unit is resistance measured?
2 What equation is used to calculate resistance?

The filament of a light bulb is made from very thin tungsten wire. Because of its resistance, it gets very hot when a current flows through.

Heating elements have resistance....   *...and so do these resistors.*

Resistors

Resistors also give off heat when a current flows through, but that isn't their job. They can be used to reduce current. In electronics circuits, like those in TVs and radios, they are used to keep currents at the right levels so that other parts work properly.

On the left, a **variable resistor** is being used to control the brightness of a bulb. The variable resistor contains a long coil of thin nichrome wire. Sliding the control to the right puts more resistance into the circuit, so the bulb gets dimmer.

Some variable resistors are rotary – you turn the control rather than slide it. Variable resistors like this are used in computer joysticks. They can also be used as volume controls, though most radios and TVs now have press buttons linked to a microchip for this.

A variable resistor (rotary type).

symbols   resistor   variable resistor   or   heater

Questions

3 On this page, there is a diagram of a circuit containing a variable resistor.

   a How is a variable resistor different from an ordinary resistor?

   b If, in the diagram, the variable resistor's control is slid to the left, what effect will this have? Give a reason for your answer.

   c Redraw the diagram so that only circuit symbols are used.

4 Why is the heating element in a hairdrier made of thin nichrome wire rather than thick copper wire?

5 Copy and complete the table below, using the resistance equation to work out the missing values:

	Resistor A	Resistor B	Resistor C
voltage across resistor in V	8	6	2
current through resistor in A	2	4	5
resistance in Ω			

More about resistance

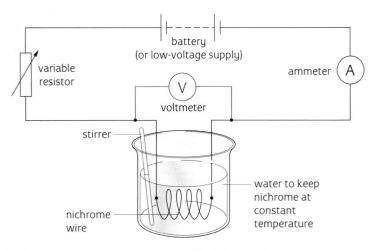

Voltage in V	Current in A	Resistance in Ω $= \dfrac{\text{voltage}}{\text{current}}$
3.0	1.0	3.0
6.0	2.0	3.0
9.0	3.0	3.0
12.0	4.0	3.0

With the circuit above, you can find how the current through a conductor depends on the voltage across it. Here, the conductor is a coil of nichrome wire, kept at a steady temperature. The table on the left gives some typical results. They show that:

- If the voltage doubles, the current doubles, and so on.
- The resistance across the nichrome wire keeps the same value, 3 Ω in this case.

If a material has the same resistance for all currents, then scientists say that it obeys **Ohm's law**. All metals obey Ohm's law – provided that their temperature doesn't change.

The resistance of a metal increases with temperature. However, the increase is small, unless the temperature rise is very large.

Resistance components

Some of the **components** (parts) used in circuits are designed to have a resistance which can vary:

Component	**Thermistor**	**Light-dependent resistor**	**Diode**
Symbol			
Resistance	High resistance when cold, low resistance when hot.	High resistance in the dark, low resistance in the light.	Very high resistance in one direction, low resistance in other.
Examples of use	In electronic circuits which detect temperature change – for example, in fire alarms or thermometers.	In electronic circuits which switch on lights automatically.	Lets current flow in one direction only. Used in power adaptors and electronic equipment.

Current–voltage graphs

With readings taken using a circuit like the one on the opposite page, current–voltage graphs can be produced for different components. Here are some examples:

A metal resistor at a steady temperature (for instance, the nichrome wire on the opposite page). The graph is a straight line through the origin. Voltage ÷ current is the same at all points. In other words, the resistance doesn't change.

A tungsten filament (in a bulb). As the current increases, the temperature rises and the resistance goes up.
Voltage ÷ current is not the same at all points. The current is not proportional to the voltage.

A diode. The current is not proportional to the voltage. And if the voltage is reversed (by connecting the diode the other way round), the current is almost zero. In effect, the diode 'blocks' current in the reverse direction.

These resistors in series...
3 Ω   6 Ω

... have the same effect as this resistance.
9 Ω

Adding resistances

If you connect more and more resistors in series, the total resistance is increased:

If resistances are connected in series:
total resistance = sum of separate resistances

For example, on the left, resistances of 3 Ω and 6 Ω in series have a total resistance of 9 Ω.

Questions

1 Name a component which:

 a has a resistance that falls as its temperature rises.

 b lets current flow through it in one direction only.

2 Look at the graph for the tungsten filament at the top of this page.

 a What is the current through the filament when the voltage across it is 2 V?

 b What is the current through the filament when the voltage across it is 12 V?

 c What is the resistance of the filament at 1500 °C?

 d What is the resistance of the filament at 3000 °C?

3 A piece of nichrome wire is kept at a steady temperature. Different voltages are put across the ends of the wire, and the current measured each time. Copy the table below and fill in the missing values:

Voltage in V	Current in A	Resistance in Ω
8	2	
4		
2		

Series and parallel circuits

The bulbs above have to get their power from the same supply. There are two ways of connecting bulbs or resistors together. The circuits below show the differences between them.

These bulbs are connected in **series**.

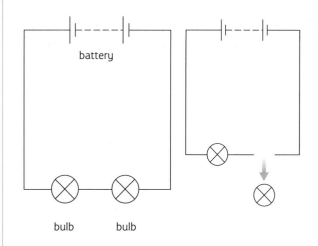

- The bulbs share the voltage from the battery, so each glows dimly.
- If one bulb is removed, the other goes out because the circuit is broken.

These bulbs are connected in **parallel**.

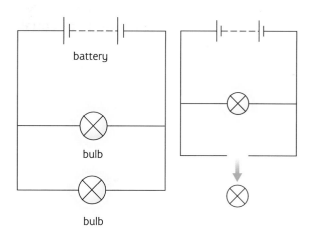

- Each bulb gets the full voltage from the battery, so each glows brightly.
- If one bulb is removed, the other keeps working because it is still part of an unbroken circuit.

If two or more bulbs have to be powered by one battery (or power supply), they are usually connected in parallel. Each bulb gets the full battery voltage. Also, each can be switched on or off by itself.

Basic circuit rules

The examples at the top of the next page show the basic rules for series and parallel circuits. But whatever the arrangement, resistance = voltage ÷ current *always* applies to *every* resistance. Check it for yourself on the resistors in the diagrams!

Questions

1 Some bulbs are to be powered by the same battery. Give *two* advantages of connecting the bulbs in parallel rather than in series.

When a battery is connected across resistors (or other components) in **series**:

- each resistor has the same current through it.
- the resistors share the battery voltage. So the voltages across them add up to equal the battery voltage.

When a battery is connected across resistors (or other components) in **parallel**:

- each resistor gets the full battery voltage.
- the resistors share the current from the battery. So the currents through them add up to equal the current from the battery.

Cell arrangements

Here are some examples of linked cells:

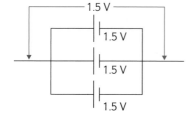

Cells in series: you add up their voltages to find the total voltage.

One cell is the wrong way round, so it cancels out one of the others.

The voltage across parallel cells is the same as from a single cell.

Questions

These questions are about the circuit on the right.

2 Will each of the bulbs A and B be ON or OFF if:

   a switch S₁ only is opened?

   b switch S₂ only is opened?

3 Bulbs A and B are identical. If both switches are closed:

   a what is the voltage across bulb A?

   b what is the current through bulb B?

   c what is the current through the battery?

4 The battery is made up of four cells.

   a What is the voltage of each cell?

   b What would the battery voltage be if one of the cells were connected the wrong way round?

2.07 Solving circuits

Sound and lighting equipment like that above contains hundreds of circuits. To produce such circuits, electrical engineers need to understand the link between voltage, current, and resistance.

Resistance–voltage–current equations

If you know the voltage across a resistor, and the current through it, you calculate the resistance with this equation:

$$\text{resistance} = \frac{\text{voltage}}{\text{current}}$$

voltage in volts (V)
current in amperes (A)
resistance in ohms (Ω)

The equation can be rearranged in two ways:

$$\text{voltage} = \text{current} \times \text{resistance}$$

$$\text{current} = \frac{\text{voltage}}{\text{resistance}}$$

These are useful if you already know the resistance, but need to find the voltage or current.

Cover 'current' if you want the equation for current. It works for voltage and resistance as well.

The triangle on the left gives all three versions of the equation.

Circuit problems

Example 1 A current of 2 A flows through a 3 Ω resistor. What is the voltage across the resistor?

In this case:

current = 2 A, resistance = 3 Ω, and voltage is to be found. So, choose the equation starting voltage = ...

$$\text{voltage} = \text{current} \times \text{resistance} = 2 \times 3 = 6\,\text{V}$$

So, the voltage across the resistor is 6 V.

Questions

1 A current of 2 A flows through a 6 Ω resistor. What is the voltage across the resistor?

battery

12 V

3 Ω

6 Ω

S

Example 2 In the circuit on the left, what is the current through: **a** the 3 Ω resistor? **b** the 6 Ω resistor? **c** the battery?

a The 3 Ω resistor has the full battery voltage across it.
So, in this case:
voltage = 12 V, resistance = 3 Ω, and current is to be found.
So, choose the equation starting current = ...

$$\text{current} = \frac{\text{voltage}}{\text{resistance}} = \frac{12}{3} = 4\,\text{A}$$

So, the current through the 3 Ω resistor is 4 A.

b The 6 Ω resistor also has the full battery voltage across it.
So you solve the problem using the same method as above.
The current through the 6 Ω resistor is 2 A.

c The battery has to supply current for *both* resistors. So:

current through battery	=	current through 6 Ω resistor	+	current through 3 Ω resistor	
	=	4 A	+	2 A	= 6 A

So, the current through the battery is 6 A.

battery

12 V

3 Ω

Example 3 In example 2 above, what is the current through the battery if the switch S is opened?

This is easier than it looks! If switch S is opened, there is no current through the 6 Ω resistor, and the circuit behaves just like the one on the left. The 3 Ω resistor still has a current of 4 A through it. So, the current through the battery is 4 A.

Questions

2 In each of the following, the resistance, voltage, or current needs to be calculated. Find the missing value:

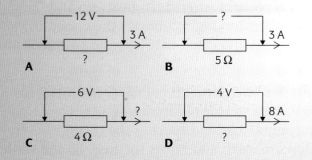

A 12 V 3 A ?

B ? 5 Ω 3 A

C 6 V 4 Ω ?

D 4 V ? 8 A

3 In the circuit below, what is the current through:
a the 2 Ω resistor?   **b** the 4 Ω resistor?
c the battery?

6 V   4 Ω   2 Ω

4 In the circuit above, if the resistors were connected in series and not parallel, what would the current through each be?

Mains electricity

Objectives

This spread should help you to

• describe a mains circuit
• describe how to wire a three-pin plug, and choose the right fuse

When you plug in a kettle, you are connecting it into a circuit. The power comes from a generator in a power station. In the UK, the **supply voltage** for mains sockets and other household circuits is 230 V.

Mains current is **alternating current (a.c.)**. It flows backwards, forwards, backwards, forwards, and so on many times per second.

Live wire This goes +, −, +, −, +, −... making the current flow backwards and forwards through the circuit.

Neutral wire This completes the circuit. It is at zero voltage.

Switch This must be fitted in the live wire so that none of the wire in the flex is still live when you switch off.

A cartridge fuse.

Fuse This is a thin piece of wire which heats up and 'blows' (melts) if the current is too high. It breaks the circuit before anything can overheat and catch fire. Like the switch, it must be in the live wire.

Earth wire This is a safety wire. It connects the metal casing of the kettle to earth and stops it becoming live. For example, if the live wire comes loose and touches the casing, a current immediately flows to earth and blows the fuse. So the kettle is then safe to touch.

Questions

1 What is the voltage at a mains socket in the UK?
2 What does a.c. stand for?
3 What is the difference between a.c. and the current that flows from a battery?
4 What does a fuse do?
5 An electric toaster has a metal casing. Why does it need an earth wire?

Three-pin plugs

Plugs are a safe and simple way of connecting appliances to the mains. In the UK, three-pin plugs are used. They have a fuse inside them:

This lamp has double insulation, so it does not need an earth wire.

Choosing the right fuse In a plug, there is usually a 3 A, 5 A, or 13 A fuse. The value tells you the current needed to blow the fuse. It should be greater than the normal current through the appliance, but as close to it as possible. For example:

If an electric toaster takes a current of 4 A, it needs a 5 A fuse. It would work with a 13 A fuse, but might not be safe. If something went wrong, its circuits might overheat and catch fire without blowing the fuse.

Double insulation

The table lamp on the left has a plastic base. This gives it an extra layer of insulation, so it does not need an earth wire. Radios and TVs also have **double insulation** like this, with no earth wire.

Questions

6 *live   neutral   earth*   Which of these wires:
   a has brown insulation?
   b is a safety wire?
   c goes alternately + and −?
   d has a blue covering?

7

   a Which of the above fuses would you choose for a fan heater taking a current of 10 A?
   b Which fuse would you choose for a food mixer taking a current of 2 A?

   c Why would you *not* use a 13 A fuse for the food mixer in part **b**?

8 The circuit below has been wrongly wired.
   a If the bulb is taken out of its socket, the circuit isn't safe. Explain why not.
   b Redraw the circuit, correctly wired.

Electrical power

The stereo systems above use energy to produce sound. But hers has more **power** than his. It uses more energy every second.

Energy is measured in **joules** (J).

Power is measured in watts (W). A power of 1 watt means that energy is being used at the rate of 1 joule every second.

So a 100 W bulb uses energy at the rate of 100 J every second. It takes 100 J of energy from the mains every second.

Electrical appliances used around the house usually have a power marked on them. You can see some examples below. Sometimes, the power is marked in **kilowatts** (kW):

$$1\,kW = 1000\,W$$

Questions

1 In what unit is power measured?

2 If a hairdrier has '1.6 kW' marked on it, what is this in watts?

kettle
2300 W

colour TV
115 W

stereo player
92 W

toaster
690 W

drill
460 W

personal stereo
1 W

12V

3A

power

voltage × current

Calculating electrical power

In circuits, power can be calculated like this:

$$\text{power} = \text{voltage} \times \text{current}$$

power in watts (W)
voltage in volts (V)
current in amperes (A)

For example, the bulb on the left has 12 V across it and a current of 3 A through it. So:

power of bulb = $12 \times 3 = 36\,\text{W}$

More equations

The power equation above can be rearranged in two ways:

$$\text{current} = \frac{\text{power}}{\text{voltage}} \qquad \text{and} \qquad \text{voltage} = \frac{\text{power}}{\text{current}}$$

These are useful if you know the power of something, but want to find the voltage or current. The triangle on the left gives all three versions of the equation.

Example A kettle has a power of 2.3 kW. What current does it take from the 230 V mains?

First, change the power into watts: 2.3 kW = 2300 W
Next, use the equation starting current =...

$$\text{current} = \frac{\text{power}}{\text{voltage}} = \frac{2300}{230} = 10\,\text{A}$$

So, the current through the kettle is 10 A.

Questions

3 You will find the three appliances below in the pictures showing typical powers on the opposite page. Calculate the power of each one, then work out what they are.

Mains voltage: 230 V		
A	**B**	**C**
current: 2 A	current: 3 A	current: 0.4 A

4 There are four appliances listed on the right.

a What is the power of each appliance in kW?

b What current is taken by each appliance?

c If you can choose between a 3 A or 13 A fuse, which type would you fit in the plug for each appliance? (Remember: the fuse value should be greater than the normal current, but as close to it as possible.)

Mains voltage: 230 V		**Power**
A	drill	460 W
B	heater	1150 W
C	travel iron	920 W
D	cassette recorder	23 W

More about the mains

Objectives

This spread should help you to
- describe how household circuits are connected
- explain the difference between a.c. and d.c.

Connecting in parallel

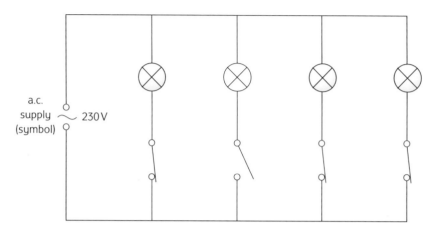

If you need to run four bulbs from the same power supply, then connecting them in parallel, as above, is the best way of doing it. Each bulb gets the full supply voltage. Also, each can be switched on and off independently without affecting the others.

In a house, the electricity supplier's cable branches into several parallel circuits. These carry power to the lights, cooker, and mains sockets. In the **consumer unit** ('fuse box'), each circuit passes through a fuse or circuit breaker (see next page). Plug-in appliances like irons and hairdriers also have a fuse in their plug.

Two-way switches

In most houses, you can turn the landing light on or off using upstairs or downstairs switches. These have two contacts instead of one. They are **two-way switches**. If both switches are up or down, then a current flows through the bulb. But if one is up and the other is down, the circuit is broken. Each switch reverses the effect of the other.

Questions

1 In a house, why are the bulbs and other mains appliances connected in parallel?

2 What would you find in a consumer unit?

Using a two-way switch.

A residual current circuit breaker (RCCB).

Circuit breakers

Some 'fuse boxes' have **circuit breakers** in them instead of fuses. A circuit breaker is an automatic switch which turns off the current if this gets too high. Unlike a fuse, it can be reset.

For extra safety, when using extension cables to lawnmowers and hedgetrimmers, you should use a **residual current circuit breaker (RCCB)**, as on the left. This detects whether any current is flowing to earth – perhaps through someone touching a wire that has been cut. It switches off the current before any harm can be done.

More about a.c. and d.c.

Alternating current (a.c.) is easier to generate than one-way **direct current** (d.c.) of the type that flows from a battery.

You can see the difference between a.c. and d.c. using an **oscilloscope**. This can plot a graph very rapidly, over and over again, showing how the voltage of a supply varies with time:

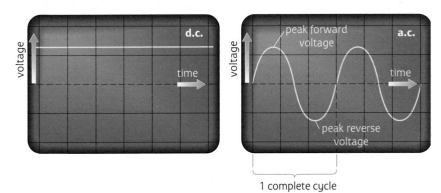

A d.c. voltage is steady, and always in the same direction. An a.c. voltage rises to a peak (maximum), falls to zero, changes direction... and so on, many times every second.

In the UK, the **mains frequency** is 50 **hertz** (Hz). This means that there are 50 complete backwards-and-forwards cycles every second.

Did you know?

Mains voltage

An a.c. voltage is always changing. But mains voltage in the UK is given as 230 V. That is because the 230 V is a special type of average. It is equal to the steady d.c. voltage which would produce the same heating effect in, for example, a kettle, iron, or toaster.

Questions

3 a What does a circuit breaker do?

   b What advantage does a circuit breaker have over a fuse?

4 Copy and complete the diagram on the right to show how the bulb can be controlled by either of the switches.

5 What is the difference between a.c. and d.c.?

6 In the UK, *mains frequency is 50 Hz.* Explain what this means.

Buying electricity

Objectives

This spread should help you to
- calculate energy in kWh
- calculate the cost of running mains appliances

Like other appliances, TVs and hairdriers take energy from the mains. That energy must be paid for, on your electricity bill.

Dan keeps his fan heater on all evening because he feels cold. Chloe uses her stereo player all day. Each thinks that the other is wasting electricity. But who is adding most to the bill? By the end of this spread, you should be able to work it out.

2 kW fan heater switched on for 5 hours

DAN

100 W stereo player switched on for 12 hours

CHLOE

Calculating energy... in joules

A heater with a power of 1 watt (W) uses 1 joule (J) of energy every second. So:

With 1 J of energy, you could run a 1 W heater for 1 second.

With 6 J of energy, you could run a 1 W heater for 6 seconds

...or a 2 W heater for 3 seconds.

In each case, you can calculate the energy in J like this:

energy	=	power	×	time
in J		in W		in seconds

Calculating energy... in kilowatt hours

Electricity supply companies measure energy in **kilowatt hours** (kW h). (1 kW h is 3600 000 J.) They charge you a set amount for each kW h supplied.

You calculate the energy in kWh like this:

energy	=	power	×	time
in kWh		in kW		in hours

For example, if a 3 kW heater is switched on for 4 hours:

energy supplied = 3 × 4 = 12 kWh

The greater the power of the appliance and the longer it is switched on for, the more energy it takes from the mains.

Questions

1   W   J   kWh

a What do the above stand for?

b Which are units of energy?

2 With 6 joules of energy, how long could you run a 3 watt heater for?

Did you know?

Counting the cost

If each kWh of energy costs 10p, then it will cost about...

5p to watch TV all evening

15p to bake a cake

30p to wash one load of clothes

240p to run a fan heater all day

The electricity bill on the right is based on the meter readings below. On many bills there is a standing (fixed) charge as well.

Central electricity

customer account no. 3742 463

present meter reading	previous meter reading	Units used	cost per Unit (£)	£
42935	41710	1225	0.10	122.50

meter reading

4 1 7 1 0

kWh

meter reading 3 months later

4 2 9 3 5

kWh

Reading the meter

The 'electricity meter' in a house is an energy meter. The more energy you take from the mains, the more you have to pay. The reading on the meter gives the total energy supplied in **Units**. The Unit is another name for the kilowatt hour.

The diagrams on the left show the meter readings at the beginning and end of a quarter (three-month period). In this case, the energy supplied in that period was 1225 Units.

If the electricity supply company charges 10p per Unit (kWh):

cost of energy supplied = 1225 × 10p = 12250p = £122.50

Cost problem

Problem If the cost of energy is 10p per Unit, how much will it cost to run a 3 kW fan heater for 4 hours?

Using the energy equation on the opposite page:

energy in kWh = 3 kW × 4 hours = 12 kWh = 12 Units

If energy is 10p per Unit: the cost of 12 Units = 12 × 10p = 120p

So, the cost of running the fan heater is 120p (£1.20).

Questions

3 Explain why a hairdrier could cost less to run than a table lamp, even though its power is greater.

4 Use the information in the table on the right to answer the following:

a How much energy does the heater take, in kWh?

b What is the cost of using the heater?

c What is the power of the lamp in kW?

d How much energy does the lamp take, in kWh?

e What is the cost of using the lamp?

	Power	Time switched on
heater	3 kW	5 hours
lamp	100 W	12 hours
cost per Unit = 10p		1 kW = 1000 W

5 Look at the information about Dan's fan heater and Chloe's stereo at the start of the spread. Work out which takes most energy from the mains.

Electric charge

Charge makes cling-film stick to your hands, and dust stick to a TV screen. It causes crackles and sparks when you comb your hair. It can even make your hair stand on end:

This person has been charged up. Her hairs all carry the same type of charge, so they repel each other (see opposite page).

Charges from the atom

Cling-film, combs, hair, and all other materials are made from atoms. Atoms all have electric charges inside them. In the centre of each atom there is a **nucleus**. This has **positive (+) charge**. Around the nucleus, there are electrons, with **negative (–) charge**.

Normally, atoms have equal amounts of negative and positive charge, so these cancel out. But electrons don't always stay attached to atoms. For example, they can be removed by rubbing.

Charging by rubbing

Insulators such as polythene and acetate can become charged when rubbed. People say that they have 'static electricity' on them.

atom

electron

nucleus

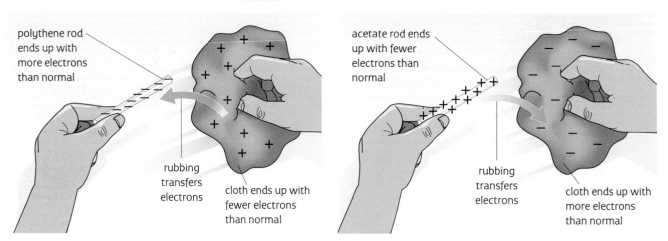

polythene rod ends up with more electrons than normal

rubbing transfers electrons

cloth ends up with fewer electrons than normal

acetate rod ends up with fewer electrons than normal

rubbing transfers electrons

cloth ends up with more electrons than normal

Questions

1 There are two different types of charge. What are they called?

2 A polythene comb becomes charged if you pull it through your hair. Where does the charge come from?

The diagrams on the previous page show what happens when polythene and acetate rods are rubbed with a woollen cloth:

When the polythene rod is rubbed, it pulls electrons from the cloth. So, overall, it ends up negatively (–) charged. The cloth is left positively (+) charged. When the acetate rod is rubbed, the effect is opposite: the cloth pulls electrons from the acetate.

The rubbing action doesn't make electric charge. It just separates charges already there. It works with insulators because, once the charges are separated, they tend to stay where they are.

Forces between charges

If charged rods are held close, there are forces between them:

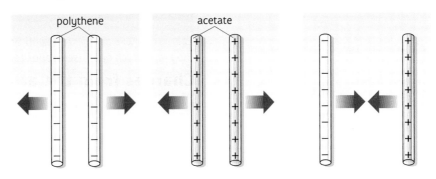

Like charges repel. Unlike charges attract.

A charged object will also attract an *uncharged* one. That is why dust is attracted to the charged screen of a TV. Being uncharged, the dust has equal amounts of + and –, so it feels attraction and repulsion. But the attracted charges are pulled slightly closer than the repelled ones, so the force on them is stronger.

Questions

3 Say whether the things below will attract each other, repel each other, or do neither:

4 A balloon becomes negatively charged when rubbed against someone's sleeve.

   a How does it becomes charged?

   b Why will it then stick to a wall?

More about charge

Objectives

This spread should help you to
- give an example of earthing
- describe how inkjet printers and photocopiers use charge
- describe how charge can pass through some liquids

Like charges repel, unlike charges attract, and charged objects attract uncharged ones. This spread looks at some effects of these forces.

Earthing

If enough charge builds up on something, electrons may be pulled through the air and cause sparks. This can be dangerous. To prevent charge building up, objects can be **earthed**: they can be connected to the ground by a conductor so that unwanted charge flows away.

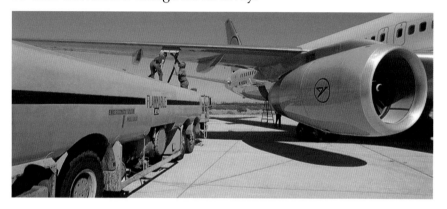

An aircraft and its tanker must be earthed during refuelling, otherwise charge might build up as the fuel 'rubs' along the pipe. One spark could be enough to ignite the fuel vapour.

Photocopiers

Photocopiers also use electric charge, but the charge comes from a power supply rather than from rubbing. Below, you can see the main stages in making a photocopy of a page with a large 'H' on it:

Inside the photocopier, a light-sensitive plate (or drum) is given a negative charge.

An image of the page is projected onto the plate. The bright areas lose their charge but the dark areas keep it.

Powdered ink (called **toner***) is attracted to the charged (dark) areas.*

A blank sheet of paper is pressed against the plate. It picks up powdered ink.

The paper is heated so that the powdered ink melts and sticks to it. The result is a copy of the original page.

Inkjet printers

An inkjet printer works by squirting tiny droplets of ink at the paper. Each produces a dot. By printing lots of dots, whole letters are formed. But to do this, the printer must control where the droplets go. It uses the force between charges to do this:

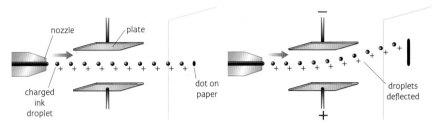

Ink droplets are charged up as they are forced out of a very narrow nozzle. The droplets pass between two metal plates. If a voltage is put across the plates, they become charged. The charged droplets are attracted to the top plate and repelled by the bottom one, so they are deflected (bent) upwards.

An inkjet printer.

Ions on the move

If an atom gains or loses electrons, it becomes charged. A charged atom (or group of atoms) is called an **ion**.

shapes are simplified and colours are false

Salty water (water with sodium chloride dissolved in it) contains ions, including those above. In the experiment on the left, a voltage has been put across the liquid. The negative ions are pulled to the **positive electrode** (+ plate), where chlorine gas is given off. The positive ions are pulled to the **negative electrode**, where hydrogen gas is given off. 'Splitting' chemical compounds in this way is called **electrolysis**. The liquid is conducting a current. However, the current is a flow of ions rather than a flow of electrons.

Questions

1 The build-up of electric charge can be dangerous.
  a Give one example of this.
  b Describe how the problem can be overcome.

2 **a** In the diagram on the right, what will happen to the droplets as they pass between the plates?
  b What difference would it make if the droplets were positively charged instead of negative?

3 What are *ions*?
4 Why can salty water conduct a current?

2.14   DANGER! Electricity

KILLER cables

A 132 000 volt overhead cable can push more than enough current through someone to kill them. To prevent accidents, the cables are suspended way above roof-top height. And the pylons are built so that people can't climb them. However, accidents have occurred when kite lines have touched cables.

DEADLY playground

Every year, over 50 children are killed or seriously injured while playing on railway lines. Electrified track is especially dangerous. Contact with the live rail doesn't always kill. But it can cause serious burns as current flows through arms or legs to the ground.

Battery *BURN*

Most people don't expect a 12 volt car battery to be dangerous. But if a spanner is accidentally connected across the wires from the battery, the surge of current could be enough to burn you or start a fire. Wise mechanics disconnect the battery before starting work.

FIRE hazards

In the home, people are more at risk from electrical fires than they are from electric shocks. Here are some of the causes:

Frayed wiring Broken strands of wire can mean that a cable has a high resistance at one point. So heat is given off when current flows through. It may be enough to melt the insulation and cause a fire.

Dirty plug pins These give a high resistance where they connect with the socket. When a current flows through, the plug may overheat.

Faulty appliances Each year, many house fires are caused by faulty washing machines and TVs. You can't tell when faults are going to develop, so the safest thing to do is not to leave appliances like this switched on when you are asleep or out of the house.

Safety first

If an accident like this happens, you must do the following before giving any help to the person:

- Switch off at the socket.
- Pull out the plug.

Talking points

See if you can find out the reason for each of the following:

- Bathroom lights have to be switched on and off by a pull-cord, rather than an ordinary switch.
- Extension leads shouldn't be coiled up tightly when in use.
- Electric lawnmowers, hedgetrimmers, and drills should always be used with a 'power breaker' safety adaptor.
- A TV set shouldn't be left on stand-by overnight or when you are out.

Lightning capital

Phoenix, Arizona, USA has been called the lightning capital of the world. If you don't like thunderstorms, stay away from Phoenix!

Lightning is caused when charge builds up on one part of a cloud and then rapidly flows – as a spark – to another cloud or the ground. But why does charge build up? A simple explanation might be that ice particles 'rub' against the air as they are sucked up through the cloud. However, the real picture is much more complicated than that.

Lightning strikes

They say that lightning never strikes twice. But that isn't true. It can strike again . . . and again.

In the First World War, Major Summerford was wounded in Flanders, not by the enemy, but by a flash of lightning which knocked him off his horse. Six years later, he was struck by lightning again while fishing – and yet again two years later when he was out for a walk. Even after his death in 1932, he did not rest in peace. Lightning shattered his tombstone.

Ions in the air

Ions are charged atoms or molecules. There are plenty floating around in the air. For example, every time there is a lightning flash, the discharge produces ions.

It has been claimed that some ions in the air improve your mood or your health, although there is no firm evidence for this. You can buy small electrical machines to ionize the air in your home. And if you think that they are going to make you feel better, you probably

Safety cage

The worker inside the cage is quite safe, despite the 2.5 million volt sparks from the huge high-voltage generator. The electric discharges strike the metal bars, rather than pass between them, so the cage has a shielding effect. In fact, if you ignore safety advice, some of the experiments done in a school laboratory can be much more dangerous than this one.

Attracting dust and ash

Some things in the house seem to attract dust. For example, you can usually see dust sticking to the screen of a TV. It is pulled there by the charge that builds up on the screen. In a house, the attraction effect may be a nuisance, but it does have practical uses elsewhere. Here is an example.

Electrostatic precipitators are fitted to the chimneys of some power stations and factories. They reduce pollution by removing tiny bits of ash from the waste gases. The diagram shows the basic layout. As the ash and waste gases pass through the chamber, the ash is given a negative charge by the wires. The charged ash is attracted to the positive plates and sticks to them. When shaken from the plates, it is collected in the tray at the bottom.

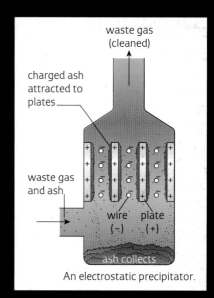

An electrostatic precipitator.

Talking points

- The electrostatic precipitator shown above makes use of the attraction between opposite charges. By looking at earlier spreads in this chapter, see if you can find some more practical uses of the forces between charges.

- When you see a flash of lightning, the 'crash' is heard a little later. By looking up information about light and sound in the index, see if you can find out why this is. With the information you have found, could you estimate how far away lightning was if the 'crash' was heard 2 seconds after the flash?

1 The circuit below can be used to test whether different materials allow an electric current to pass through or not:

battery

bulb

material being tested

a Will the bulb light up when each of the following materials is connected between the clips? (Answer each with a YES or NO.)
 i Iron
 ii Plastic
 iii Glass
 iv Copper
 v Aluminium

b What name is given to a material that:
 i lets an electric current pass through?
 ii stops an electric current passing through?

2 The diagrams below show some circuit symbols.

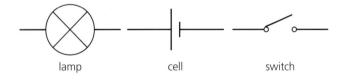

lamp   cell   switch

a i Draw in your books a circuit diagram showing two lamps, one cell and a switch connected in series.

b i Now draw a circuit diagram showing two lamps in parallel, together with a cell and a switch that works both lamps.

c i Draw a circuit diagram showing two lamps in parallel, together with a cell and a switch that works *one* of the lamps.

 ii Show on your last diagram where an ammeter should be placed to measure the current in the cell.

3 Use your ideas about electrons to explain each of the following:
 a Electrons are pushed out of the negative (–) terminal of a battery, not the positive (+).
 b If you rub a polythene rod with a piece of cloth, the rod ends up with negative charge (–), while the cloth is left with an equal amount of positive charge (+).

4 These wires are made of the same material. They all have resistance.

A

B

C

 a Which wire has most resistance?
 b Which wire has least resistance?

5 The diagram below shows two resistors connected in series.

A   2 Ω   4 Ω   B

 a Calculate the total resistance between A and B.
 b Draw in your books a circuit diagram which shows two $1\frac{1}{2}$V cells, a switch and the above two resistors all connected in series. Calculate the current that flows around the circuit.

6 a Below, ammeters are being used to measure the current in different parts of a circuit.

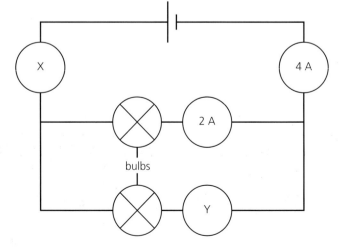

X

4 A

2 A

bulbs

Y

i Have the bulbs been connected to the battery in *series* or in *parallel*?

ii What is the reading on ammeter X? Give a reason for your answer.

iii What is the reading on ammeter Y? Give a reason for your answer.

iv If one of the bulbs is removed, so that there is a gap between its connecting wires, what will be the effect on the other bulb?

7 Below, voltmeters are being used to measure the voltage across different parts of a circuit.

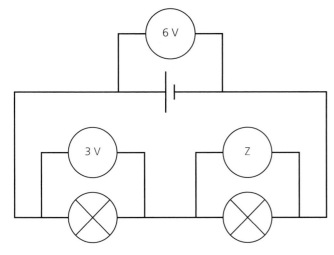

i Have the bulbs been connected to the battery in *series* or in *parallel*?

ii What is the reading on voltmeter Z? Give a reason for your answer.

iii If one of the bulbs is removed, so that there is a gap between its connecting wires, what will be the effect on the other bulb?

8 Two families A and B each bought a set of Christmas tree lights and assembled them according to the instructions enclosed.

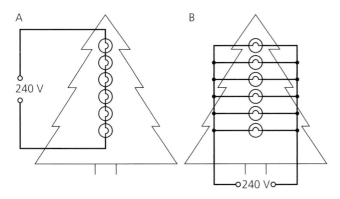

i After a while one bulb in each tree blows.

  a What happens to Family A's lights?

  b What happens to Family B's lights?

  c With each set of lights there is a spare bulb. Explain clearly what each family must do to find and replace their faulty bulb.

ii Each of Family A's bulbs has 10 W written on it whilst those of Family B have 20 W on them.

  a Whose bulbs are brightest? Explain your answer.

  b What is the voltage across each of the bulbs on

    1 Family A's tree?

    2 Family B's tree?

  c What is the current flowing through each of the bulbs on

    1 Family A's tree?

    2 Family B's tree?

  d Would a 13 ampere fuse be suitable for either of these circuits? Explain your answer.

9 In the circuit below, a 6 V battery has been connected to a 3 Ω resistor:

  a What is the current in the circuit?

  b What is the power output of the battery?

10 A man uses 2 kW kettle to boil some water.

It takes 6 minutes to boil the water.

i Calculate the energy transferred in **kilowatt-hours**.

energy in kW h = power in kW × time in hours

ii Electricity costs 12p per kW h.

How much does it cost the man to boil the water?

11 A low-energy light bulb has a power rating of only 20 W, but produces the same amount of light as an ordinary 100 W bulb. Both bulbs are to be switched on for 1000 hours.

100 W = 20 W

ordinary bulb   low-energy bulb

a What is the power of each bulb in kW?

b How much energy (in kW h) will the low-energy bulb use in 1000 hours?

c How much energy (in kW h) will the ordinary energy light bulb use in 1000 hours?

d If electricity costs 10p per unit (kW h), how much money will be saved on electricity bills over a 1000-hour period by using the low-energy bulb instead of the ordinary bulb?

e The ordinary bulb uses more energy than the low-energy one for the same amount of light. What happens to the extra energy supplied?

12 The diagram below shows the wiring of a 13A, three-pin plug.

i Copy and complete the table below stating the name and colour of the three wires labelled A, B and C. Part of the table has already been completed for you.

Wire	Name	Colour
A		
B	Earth	
C		

ii Describe and explain the function of wire **B**.

iii Many domestic appliances are marked with the symbol ▣ which means they are double insulated and require only two wires.

Which **one** of the three wires listed above is not required?

Explain how double insulation makes this possible.

13 This plug is dangerous.

yellow/green

brown

fuse

blue

cable grip

cable

Describe **three** things that make the plug **unsafe**.

14 The fan heater below runs on the 230 V mains. It has two heating elements, each taking a current of 4 A, and a fan taking a current of 0.5 A.

S_1 S_2 S_3

fan heater

heating elements

metal case   earth   fan motor

earth

plug

Y

X

a Which switch should be closed if you want:

i the fan only, for cool air?

ii the fan and one element?

b If the fan heater is on full power, how much current flows from the mains?

c What fuse should be fitted in the plug, 3 A or 13 A?

d Which terminal in the plug is live?

e Why is the earth connection needed?

f What colour cable should be connected to terminal X?

g What colour cable should be connected to terminal Y?

h Give reasons for each of the following:

i If an appliance takes a current of 2 A, you should not fit a 13 A fuse in its plug.

ii Some appliances, such as radios and hairdryers, do not need an earth wire.

15 i What is the principal energy transformation which takes place when a 2 kW, 230 V, two bar electric fire is turned on?

ii What is the power rating of the fire? Write a sentence explaining exactly what your answer means.

iii To which part of the electric fire is the earth wire always connected? Explain what might happen if the fire became faulty and there was no earth wire.

iv Where should the switch for turning the fire on and off be positioned? Explain your answer.

v From the figures given in **i** calculate the current flowing through the fire.

vi What is the most appropriate fuse for this circuit?

vii Why would it be dangerous to connect two fires like the one described above to the same socket in a ring main?

viii If any electrical appliance is found to be faulty when it is switched on, what is the first thing you must do?

16 a Describe one method of producing static electricity. Include diagrams with your explanation.

The picture below shows an aircraft being refuelled.

b Explain how electrostatic charge can build up during refuelling.

c During refuelling, a copper wire is connected between the aircraft and the tanker. Without the wire a charge would build up on the aircraft.

i Why is a build-up of charge on the aircraft dangerous?

ii What happens to any charge which builds up on the aircraft during refuelling?

fuel tank

copper wire

fuel pipe

not to scale

Key words

The spread numbers in brackets tell you where to find more information.

alternating current (a.c.) Current which flows backwards and forwards, backwards and forwards... and so on. Mains current is like this. *(2.08, 2.10)*

ammeter An instrument that measures current, in amperes (A). *(2.02)*

ampere (A) Unit of electric current. *(2.02)*

battery A collection of electric cells – although the word is commonly used for a single cell as well. *(2.01, 2.03)*

cell A device that pushes current round a circuit when chemicals inside it react. *(2.01, 2.03)*

charge This is carried by some of the particles in atoms. There are two types: positive (+) and negative (–). *(2.01, 2.12 – 2.13, 8.01)*

conductor (electrical) A material that lets an electric current flow through it. Metals are the best conductors. *(2.01)*

current A flow of charge. It is measured in amperes (A). *(2.02)*

diode A component that allows current to flow through it in one direction but not the other. *(2.05)*

direct current (d.c.) Current which always flows in the same direction. The current from a battery is like this. *(2.10)*

electrolysis Process in which chemical changes occur when a current flows through a liquid. *(2.13)*

electron A negatively (–) charged particle from the atom. In a circuit, the 'electricity' in the wires is a flow of electrons. *(2.01, 8.01)*

fuse A small piece of wire that overheats, melts, and breaks a circuit if the current gets too high. *(2.08)*

insulator (electrical) A material that does not let an electric current flow through it. *(2.01)*

ion Electrically charged atom (or group of atoms). *(2.13, 8.02)*

kilowatt hour (kWh) Unit of energy used by electricity supply companies. It is the energy taken in 1 hour by an appliance with a power of 1 kW. *(2.11)*

light-dependent resistor (LDR) A component whose resistance varies as it gets lighter or darker. *(2.05)*

ohm (Ω) Unit of electrical resistance. *(2.04)*

power The rate at which an an appliance transforms energy (changes it into another form). It is measured in watts (W). 1 watt is equal to 1 joule per second. *(2.09, 6.06)*

resistance This is measured in ohms (W). The higher the resistance of a conductor, the less current flows through it for each volt across it. *(2.04)*

thermistor A component that has a large change in resistance when its temperature changes. *(2.05)*

volt (V) Unit of voltage. *(2.03)*

voltage The higher a battery's voltage, the more energy is given to each electron pushed out into the circuit. The higher the voltage across a bulb (or other component), the more energy is spent by each electron as it passes through. *(2.03)*.

voltmeter An instrument that measures voltage, in volts (V). *(2.03)*

watt (W) Unit of power. It is equal to 1 joule per second. *(2.09, 6.06)*

Forces and motion

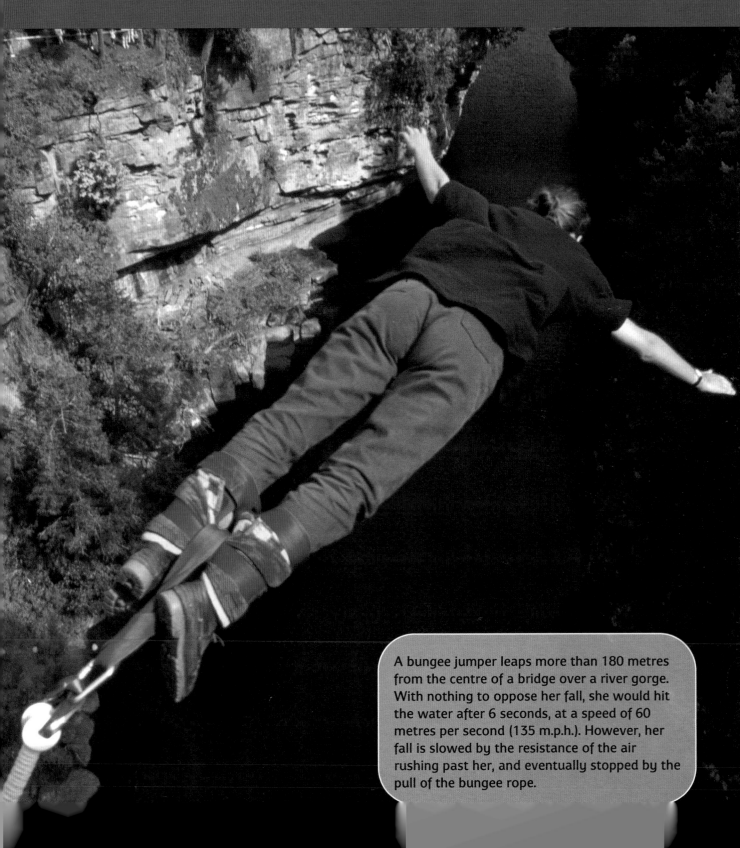

A bungee jumper leaps more than 180 metres from the centre of a bridge over a river gorge. With nothing to oppose her fall, she would hit the water after 6 seconds, at a speed of 60 metres per second (135 m.p.h.). However, her fall is slowed by the resistance of the air rushing past her, and eventually stopped by the pull of the bungee rope.

Speed

Here is a simple method of measuring speed. You could use it to work out the speed of a cyclist like the one below:

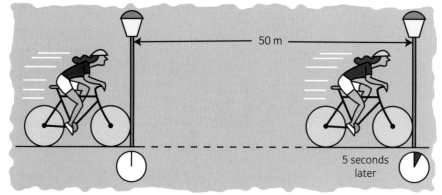

Measure the distance between two points on a road, say two lamp posts, as above. Measure the time taken to travel between these points. Then use this equation:

$$\text{speed} = \frac{\text{distance travelled}}{\text{time taken}}$$

distance in metres (m)
time in seconds (s)
speed in metres per second (m/s)

If the cyclist travels 50 m in 5 s her speed is 50/5, which is 10 m/s.

This calculation really gives her average speed, as her actual speed may vary during the 5 s. To find an actual speed, you need to know the distance travelled in the shortest time you can measure.

Velocity

Velocity means speed in a particular direction. To show the direction, you can use an arrow. Or, in simple cases, you can use a + or − to show whether the motion is to the right or to the left. There are some examples below. (A velocity of +10 m/s may be written without the +, just as 10 m/s.)

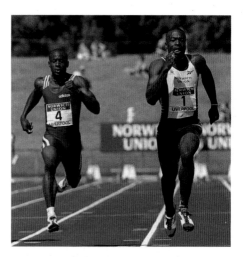

A world-class 100 metre sprinter has an average speed of about 10 m/s (or 22 miles per hour (m.p.h.)).

Questions

1 If a cyclist travels 40 metres in 8 seconds, what is her average speed?

2 What is the difference between *speed* and *velocity*?

2 m/s²

time in s	velocity in m/s
0	0
1	2
2	4
3	6
4	8

The velocity of this car is increasing by 2 m/s every second. The acceleration is 2 m/s².

Acceleration

Something is **accelerating** if its velocity is *changing*. The velocity of the car on the left is increasing by 2 m/s every second. The car has an acceleration of 2 metres per second per second, written 2 m/s². Acceleration is calculated like this:

$$\text{acceleration} = \frac{\text{change in velocity}}{\text{time taken}}$$

velocity in m/s
time in s
acceleration in m/s²

In simple cases, where something is always travelling in the same direction, 'change in velocity' means the same thing as 'gain in speed'. For example, the car above left has a change in velocity of 8 m/s in 4 s. In other words, its speed goes up by 8 m/s in 4 s. So: acceleration = 8/4 = 2 m/s².

Retardation

Retardation means 'deceleration'. If a car has a retardation of 2 m/s², its velocity is getting *less* by 2 m/s every second.

A retardation of 2 m/s² means the same as an acceleration of –2 m/s². Either way, the velocity is reducing by 2 m/s every second.

The Space Shuttle uses a parachute, as well as its brakes, to produce the retardation it needs when it lands.

Questions

3 A car has an acceleration of 4 m/s². Explain what this means.

Questions 4–10 are about the table below, which shows how the speed of a car changed with time.

4 What was the car's maximum speed?

5 For how many seconds was the car accelerating?

6 When was the car's acceleration zero ?

7 What was the change in speed in the first 3 seconds?

8 What was the acceleration over the first 3 seconds?

9 How many seconds after the start of its journey did the car start to brake?

10 What was the retardation over the last 4 seconds?

Time in seconds	0	1	2	3	4	5	6	7	8	9	10	11	12	13	14	15
Speed in m/s	0	3	6	9	12	12	12	12	12	12	10	8	6	4	2	0

Changing positions

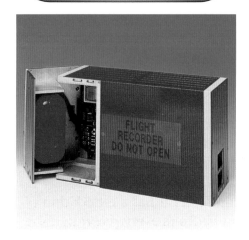

A 'black box' flight recorder isn't black at all!

Large passenger aircraft carry 'black box' flight recorders like the one on the left. One job of a recorder is to record – on magnetic wire – the position of the aircraft throughout the flight. In the very unlikely event of a crash, the box is tough enough to survive. Engineers can use data from it to work out how fast the aircraft was travelling before the accident, how the speed and direction were changing, and whether this was normal.

Trolley experiments

Below, you can see a simpler method of recording motion, using paper tape. The 'vehicle' being studied is a trolley moving on a laboratory bench. As the trolley is pulled across the bench, it trails a paper tape behind it. The tape passes through a timer. This marks dots on the tape at regular intervals of time (every 1/50 second).

trolley pulled
across bench

ticker-tape timer

paper tape

50 dots punched on
tape every second

On the next page are the results of five different 'runs' with the trolley. For each one, you can work out the motion of the trolley by seeing how the distance between the dots changes. The faster the trolley, the further it travelled in each 1/50 second, so the bigger the distance between the dots.

start

steady speed: distance between dots stays the same

higher steady speed: distance between dots greater than before

acceleration: distance between dots increases

acceleration ...   ... then ...   ... retardation (deceleration)

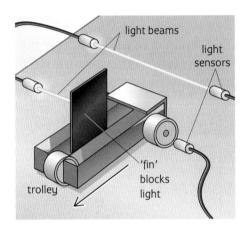

More trolley experiments

The motion of a trolley can also be studied using light sensors linked to a datalogger. The datalogger is connected to a computer so that its results can be displayed as a graph.

The trolley on the left has a 'fin' on the top. As the fin moves past each sensor, the module measures the time for which the light beam is blocked: the faster the trolley, the shorter the time. The computer can use this information to work out the speed of the trolley. Using measurements taken at different positions along the bench, it can show how the speed of the trolley changed.

Questions

1 Tapes A–D below are from trolley experiments. Which one shows each of the following?

  a Acceleration, then a steady speed.

  b A steady speed, then retardation (deceleration) until stopped.

  c A steady speed, then acceleration, then a higher steady speed.

2 A trolley travelling at a steady speed loses speed, stops, then accelerates. Copy the blank tape below. Mark in the pattern of dots you might expect to see.

Motion graphs

From motion graphs, you can work out how fast something is moving, and whether it is accelerating.

Distance–time graphs

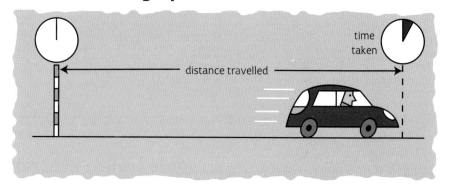

The car above is travelling along a straight road. Every second (s), its distance from the post is measured, in metres (m). Here are four examples of the graphs you might get from the readings:

A *Car travelling at a **steady speed***

time in s	distance in m
0	0
1	10
2	20
3	30
4	40
5	50

speed = 10 m/s

The line rises 10 m on the distance scale for every 1 s on the time scale. So the speed is 10 m/s.

B *Car travelling at a **higher steady speed***

time in s	distance in m
0	0
1	20
2	40
3	60
4	80
5	100

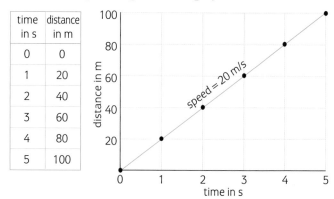

speed = 20 m/s

The line is steeper. It rises 20 m on the distance scale for every 1 s on the time scale. So the speed is 20 m/s.

C *Car **accelerating***

time in s	distance in m
0	0
1	10
2	25
3	45
4	70
5	100

line getting steeper speed increasing

The speed rises. So the car travels further each second than the one before, and the line curves upwards.

D *Car **stationary** (stopped)*

time in s	distance in m
0	50
1	50
2	50
3	50
4	50
5	50

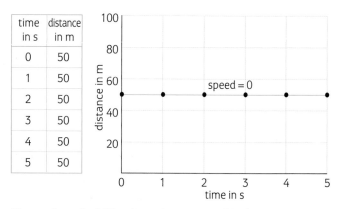

speed = 0

The car is parked 50 m from the post, so this distance stays the same.

Speed–time graphs

Below are two examples of the graphs you might get if you measure the speed of a car every second as it travels along a straight road.

Don't confuse these graphs with distance–time graphs! The shapes may look the same, but their meaning is very different.

E *Car travelling at a **steady speed***

time in s	speed in m/s
0	15
1	15
2	15
3	15
4	15
5	15

The speed stays the same, so the line stays at the same level.

F *Car **accelerating***

time in s	speed in m/s
0	0
1	4
2	8
3	12
4	16
5	20

As the car gains speed, the line rises 4 m/s on the speed scale for every 1 s on the time scale.

Velocity–time graphs The graphs above could have their vertical axis labelled 'velocity in m/s' rather than 'speed in m/s'. In simple cases, where something is always travelling in the same direction, a speed–time graph and a velocity–time graph look exactly the same.

Questions

To answer these questions, you will need the equations for speed and for acceleration in the previous spread. So write these down before you start.

1

The speed–time graph above is for a motor cycle travelling along a straight road.

a What is the motor cycle doing betweens points
  i P and Q?   **ii** Q and R?   **iii** R and S?

b What is the motor cycle's maximum speed?

c For how many seconds is the motor cycle moving?

d How much speed does it gain in the first 10 seconds?

e What is the acceleration in the first 10 seconds?

2

The distance–time graph above is for another motor cycle travelling along a straight road.

a What is the motor cycle doing between points **D** and **E** on the graph?

b What is the speed of the motor cycle between **B** and **C**?

3.04

Forces and gravity

Objectives

This spread should help you to

- give examples of forces and how they are measured
- explain what weight and gravitational field strength are

Did you know?

Typical forces

Force to switch on a bathroom light...	10 N
Force to pull open a drinks can...	20 N
Force to lift a heavy suitcase...	200 N
Force from a jet engine...	250 000 N

A **force** is a push or pull. It is measured in **newtons** (N). You can see some typical force values in the table below left.

Small forces can be measured using a spring balance (called a **newtonmeter**) like the one at the bottom of the page. The greater the force, the more the spring is stretched, and the higher the reading on the scale.

Here are some examples of forces:

Tension *The force in a stretched material.*

Weight *The downward pull of gravity.*

Friction *The force that tries to stop one thing sliding past another.*

Air resistance *Another type of friction.*

Gravitational force

If you hang something from the end of a spring balance, as on the left, you can measure a downward pull from the Earth. The pull is called a **gravitational force**.

No one knows what causes gravitational force. But several things are known about it:

- All masses attract each other. The greater the masses, the stronger the force.
- The closer the masses, the stronger the force.

The force between everyday objects is far too weak to measure. It only becomes strong if one of the objects has a huge mass, like the Earth.

Weight and gravitational field strength

Weight is another name for the gravitational force from the Earth. It is measured in N, just like other forces.

The more mass something has, the more it weighs.

Questions

1 *kg N*
What do each of the above stand for?

2 Which of the above would you use to measure:

a mass?

b force?

c weight?

On Earth, each kilogram (kg) of matter weighs 10 N. The Earth has a **gravitational field strength** of 10 newtons per kilogram (N/kg). This is called **g**.

If you know the mass of something, you can work out its weight like this:

weight = mass × g
in N   in kg

where g is 10 N/kg on Earth.

For example, the person in the diagram above has a mass of 50 kg.

So:
weight =   50   ×   10   =   500 N

People often use the word 'weight' when they really mean 'mass'. The person above doesn't 'weigh' 50 kg. He has a *mass* of 50 kg and a *weight* of 500 N.

Questions

3 In the diagram on the right, a climber is swinging on a rope, and moving fast.

Draw a simple version of the diagram.

Show *three* forces acting on the climber.

Name the three forces by labelling them.

4 Work out the weights of each of the masses below, assuming that g is 10 N/kg.

Friction

Friction is the force that tries to stop materials sliding past each other. There is friction between your hands when you rub them together, and friction between your shoes and the ground when you walk along. Air resistance is another type of friction. It slows you down when you ride a bike.

Friction can be useful or it can be a nuisance. Here are some examples, on a bike:

Friction a nuisance — Friction useful

air resistance — saddle — handlebar grips — brakes — bearings — tyres — pedals

Parts of a car wheel (see question **3**).

roller bearing — disc — grease — brake pad — tyre — shaft

Using friction

Without friction between the tyres and the ground, you would not be able to ride a bike. It would be like riding on ice. You could not speed up, turn, or stop.

Brakes rely on friction. The wheels of a cycle are slowed by pressing rubber blocks against the rims. The wheels of a car are slowed by pressing fibre pads against metal discs attached to the wheels. But none of these brakes would be any good without friction between the tyres and the ground.

Problems with friction

Friction slows moving things and produces heat. In machinery, grease and oil are used to reduce friction so that moving parts do not overheat and seize up. Ball bearings and roller bearings also reduce friction. Their rolling action means that a wheel does not rub against its shaft.

Questions

1 Give one place on a bike where friction is a nuisance.

2 Give one place on a bike where friction is needed. Say *why* the friction is needed there.

Friction from air and water

Air and water 'rub' against things when they they flow past them. For example, when a car is travelling fast, air resistance is by far the largest frictional force pulling against it.

If a car could speed along without air resistance, it would use much less fuel. Car designers cannot get rid of air resistance, but they can give the car a streamlined shape to reduce it as much as possible.

Air resistance increases with speed. So drivers can reduce air resistance and save fuel by not driving so fast.

Reducing friction from air. Car bodies are specially shaped to smooth the airflow past them and reduce air resistance. A low 'front-on' area also helps.

Reducing friction from water. When this hydrofoil is going fast, it rises up on 'water skis' to reduce the friction between its hull and the water.

Questions

3 Look at the diagram on the opposite page, showing the parts of a car wheel.

   a Give *two* places on the wheel where friction is useful.

   b Give *one* place where friction is a nuisance.

   c What features does the wheel have to reduce friction at the place you chose in part **b**?

   d Give *two* reasons why it is important to reduce the friction at the place you chose in part **b**.

4 Look at the photograph on the right. List the features you can see for reducing friction.

5 Cars are slowed down by the force of air resistance.

   a Describe *two* ways in which the force of air resistance on a car can be reduced.

   b What are the advantages of reducing air resistance on a car?

Balanced forces

Objectives

This spread should help you to

• describe how stationary and moving things behave if there are no forces on them, or if the forces are balanced

No one is winning the tug-of-war match above, and the knot in the middle doesn't move. The two forces on it are balanced. They cancel each other out. Their combined effect is zero.

This spread is about how things behave when there are no forces acting, or the forces are balanced.

Balanced forces when still

When the girl is stationary, the forces on her are balanced.

When the girl stands on the beam, it bends, until the springiness of the wood produces enough upward force to support her weight. Then, the forces on the girl are balanced, and she is stationary (still). The floor isn't as springy as the beam, but it too produces an upward force to equal the girl's weight when she stands on it.

Newton's first law of motion

On Earth, unpowered vehicles quickly come to rest – slowed by the force of friction. But how would they behave if there were *no* forces acting? According to Sir Isaac Newton's **first law of motion:**

> If something has no force on it, it will...
>
> ...if still, stay still;
> ...if moving, keep moving at a steady velocity (steady speed in a straight line).

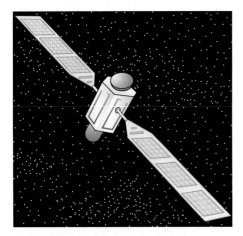

Deep in space, with no frictional forces to slow it down, an unpowered spacecraft will keep moving for ever.

Balanced forces when moving

If something is moving, and the forces on it are balanced, it behaves as if there is no force acting. It keeps moving at a steady speed in a straight line, as predicted by Newton's first law. Here are two examples of moving things with balanced forces on them:

A skydiver with steady velocity (steady speed in a straight line).

A skater with steady velocity (steady speed in a straight line).

When a skydiver is falling at her terminal speed, the forces on her are balanced.

Terminal speed

A skydiver jumps from a helicopter. As her speed rises, the air resistance on her increases until it matches her weight. Then, the two forces are balanced, and she reaches a steady speed. This is called her **terminal speed** (or **terminal velocity**). It is usually about 60 m/s (120 m.p.h.), though the actual value depends on air conditions, as well as the size, shape, and weight of the skydiver.

When the skydiver opens her parachute, the extra area of material increases the air resistance. So she loses speed rapidly until the forces are again in balance at a new, slower, terminal speed.

Questions

1 If the forces on something are balanced, which of the following could it be doing? (There may be more than one answer.)

 a speeding up   **b** slowing down

 c staying still   **d** moving at a steady speed in a straight line

2 The parachutist on the right is descending at a steady speed.

 a What name is given to this speed?

 b Copy the diagram. Mark in and label another force acting.

c How does this force compare with the weight?

d If the parachutist used a larger parachute, how would this affect the steady speed reached? Explain why.

weight

3.07   Unbalanced forces

3.07

Unbalanced forces

Objectives

This spread should help you to

- describe how things behave if the forces on them are unbalanced

On Earth, most things have more than one force on them. For example, a falling stone has weight and air resistance. This spread is about how things behave when the forces on them are unbalanced.

Resultant force

If the forces on something are unbalanced, they have a combined effect called the **resultant** force. The chart below gives some examples of the resultant of two forces. (N = newton.)

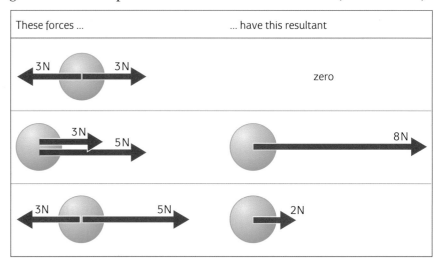

These forces …	… have this resultant
3N ← ● → 3N	zero
● 3N → 5N →	● ———→ 8N
3N ← ● 5N →	● → 2N

Mass and motion

All things resist a change in speed – even if their speed is zero. If an object is at rest, it takes a force to make it move. If it is moving, it takes a force to make it go faster or slower.

The more mass something has, the more it resists any change in motion. In other words, the more difficult it is to accelerate.

Questions

1 A stone has two forces on it: 10N downwards and 4N upwards.

   a Draw a diagram to show the forces on the stone.

   b What is the resultant force?

   c What is the direction of this force?

This tanker has so much mass that, once it is moving, it is extremely difficult to stop.

The effect of a resultant force

Imagine a truck on a road...

If there is a resultant force on the truck, it will accelerate – in the same direction as this force.

Increasing the resultant force produces more acceleration.

But if the mass of the truck is increased, you get less acceleration for the same force.

Questions

2 Diagram **A** on the right shows two forces on a car.

  a What is the direction of the resultant force?

  b Would you expect the car to *gain speed* or *lose speed*?

  c If the car had more mass, what effect would this have?

  d If the resultant force on the car were greater, what effect would this have?

3 Diagram **B** on the right shows two forces on another car.

  a What is the direction of the resultant force?

  b Would you expect this car to *gain speed* or *lose speed*? Give a reason for your answer.

c What would the car do if the two forces were equal?

Speed and safety

Objectives

This spread should help you to

- describe the factors which affect a car's stopping distance
- describe features which can make a car safer for its passengers

Stopping distance

In an emergency, the driver of a car may have to react quickly and apply the brakes to stop the car.

A car's **stopping distance** depends on two things:

- The **thinking distance**. This is how far the car travels *before* the brakes are applied, while the driver is still reacting.
- The **braking distance**. This is how far the car then travels, *after* the brakes have been applied.

It takes an average driver more than half a second to react and press the brake pedal. This is the driver's **reaction time**. During this time, the car does not slow down. For example:

If a car has a speed of 20 m/s (metres per second), and the driver has a reaction time of 0.5 s, the car will travel 10 m in that time. At a higher speed, the thinking distance would be greater.

The chart above shows the stopping distances for a car at different speeds. They are average figures for a dry road. The actual stopping distance may be *greater*. Here are some of the reasons why:

The *driver* may have a slower reaction time, because of...

- tiredness
- poor weather conditions affecting visibility
- the effects of alcohol or drugs

The *brakes* may take longer to stop the car, because of...

- a wet or icy road
- a heavy load in the car
- worn brakes or tyres

Questions

1 For a car, what is meant by each of these?
  a thinking distance
  b braking distance
  c stopping distance
2 Give *two* reasons why the thinking distance may be greater than normal.

If there isn't enough friction between its tyres and the road, a car will skid.

Braking, friction, and skidding

To stop quickly, a car must lose speed rapidly. A high braking force is needed for this. It is provided by the friction between the tyres and the road. But there is a limit to the amount of friction ('grip') that the tyres can supply. If the brakes are put on too strongly, the wheels will 'lock up' (stop turning) and the car will skid.

Safety features

In a collision, a car stops, but its passengers keep moving... until something stops them as well. The 'something' could be the steering wheel or windscreen, and the impact could cause injury or death. That is why modern cars have these safety features:

Seat belts These stop the passengers hitting the windscreen or other hard parts of the car's inside.

Air bags These inflate in a collision. They cushion the passengers from the effects of any impact.

Crumple zone The front section of a car is a 'crumple zone'. It is designed to collapse steadily in a crash so that the seat belts and air bags can slow the passengers less violently.

This test shows how a car's front 'crumple zone' collapses in a collision so that the impact is less violent for the passengers. (The passenger compartment forms a rigid cage which is designed not to collapse.)

Questions

3 Describe *three* features that a modern car has to make the effects of a collision less harmful to the passengers.

4 Cutting your speed is the best safety feature of all. Which of the following are reduced if a car travels more slowly? (You can choose more than one answer.)

   a Driver's reaction time
   b Thinking distance
   c Braking distance
   d Risk of serious injury

5 In the chart on the opposite page, what is the thinking distance: **a** at 25 m/s?   **b** at 30 m/s?

6 Alcohol slows people's reactions. If a driver has a reaction time of 2 s, what will his thinking distance be at 25 m/s (56 m.p.h)?
   (You may need an equation from the box below to answer this.)

$$\text{speed} = \frac{\text{distance}}{\text{time}} \qquad \text{So: distance} = \text{speed} \times \text{time}$$

distance in metres (m); time in seconds (s); speed in m/s.

Action and reaction

Objectives

This spread should help you to

- explain how forces always occur in pairs, with one force acting on one object and its equal but opposite partner on another

Forces are always pushes or pulls between *two* things. So they always occur in pairs. One force acts on one thing. Its equal but opposite partner acts on the other. The paired forces are known as the **action** and the **reaction**. But it doesn't matter which you call which. One cannot exist without the other.

Here are some examples of action–reaction pairs:

Earth pulls downwards on skydiver

skydiver pulls upwards on Earth

runner pushes backwards on ground

ground pushes forwards on runner

forward force on bullet: bullet shoots out

backward force on gun: gun recoils

Newton's third law of motion

Sir Isaac Newton was the first to realise that forces occur in pairs. Here is his **third law of motion**, in two versions:

> For every action there is an equal and opposite reaction.
>
> or
>
> If A pushes on B, then B pushes on A with an equal but opposite force.

If forces always occur in pairs, why don't they cancel each other out?

ANSWER

The two forces act on different things, not the same thing.

If falling things are pulled downwards by gravity, why isn't the Earth pulled upwards?

ANSWER

It is! But the Earth is so massive that the upward force on it has too small an effect to be noticed.

A rocket. As hot gas is pushed downwards, the rocket is pushed upwards.

Rockets and jets

Rockets and jets use the action–reaction idea. They push out a huge mass of gas in one direction so that they get pushed in the opposite direction.

Rocket engines have a combustion chamber where fuel is mixed with oxygen, and burnt. This produces lots of hot gas, which expands and rushes out of the nozzle.

In a rocket, the fuel and oxygen are stored either as cold liquids, or in chemicals which have been compressed into solid pellets.

Jet engines also push out lots of gas. But the gas is mainly air, drawn in by a huge fan.

Most of the air is pushed out by the fan. But some goes into the part of the engine that drives the fan. This is how it is used. The air is compressed, then mixed with fuel in a combustion chamber, so that the fuel burns violently. This produces lots of hot gas, which expands and rushes out of the engine. As it does so, it pushes a turbine round. The spinning turbine drives the compressor and the fan.

A jet engine. As air and hot gas are pushed backwards, the engine is pushed forwards.

Questions

1 The person on the right weighs 500N (newtons). The diagram shows the force of his feet pressing on the ground.

 a Copy the diagram. Label the size of the force (in N).

 b The ground pushes on the person's feet. Draw in this force and label its size (in N).

2 When a gun is fired, it pushes the bullet forwards. Why does the gun recoil backwards?

3 In the diagram on the opposite page, the forces on a runner and on the ground are equal. The runner moves forwards, but the ground doesn't seem to move backwards. Why not?

Turning and balancing

Forces can have a turning effect. In the diagram below, someone is using a spanner to turn a bolt. With a longer spanner, they could use the same force to produce an even greater turning effect.

The strength of a turning effect is called a **moment**. It can be calculated with this equation:

$$\text{moment} = \text{force} \times \text{distance from turning point}$$

The distance is the *shortest* distance from the turning point to the line of the force. A turning point is also known as a **pivot**.

0.2 m

turning point

moment = 10 × 0.2
= 2 Nm

10 N

this spanner has twice the turning effect
0.4 m

moment = 10 × 0.4
= 4 Nm

10 N

Moments in balance

Below, a plank has been balanced on a log. Weights have been put on the plank, and placed so that it still balances. One weight has a turning effect to the left, the other to the right. The two turning effects are equal, and cancel out. That is why the plank balances.

According to the **law of moments**, if something balances:

moment turning to the left	=	moment turning to the right

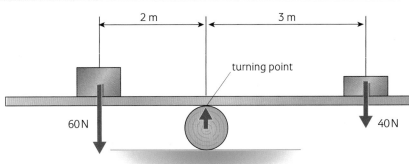

2 m   3 m

turning point

60 N   40 N

moment (to left)
= 60 × 2 = 120 Nm

these are equal

moment (to right)
= 40 × 3 = 120 Nm

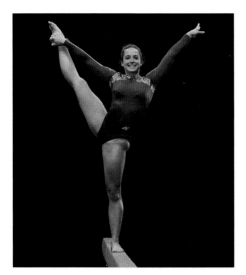

To balance on a beam, you have to keep your centre of mass over the beam. Otherwise your weight will have a turning effect and pull you over.

Centre of mass

total weight of different parts = weight of whole body

centre of gravity

All the bits of your body have weight. Together, these tiny weights act like a single force pulling at just one point. This point is called your **centre of mass** (or **centre of gravity**). Simple shapes, such as a metre rule, often have a centre of mass exactly in the middle.

If you suspend a piece of card from some thread, it always hangs with its centre of mass in line with the thread. You can use this idea to find the centre of mass.

Suspend the card from one corner and draw a vertical line from it. Do the same using another corner. Then see where the two lines cross. This is the centre of mass.

Questions

3 In diagram **A** on the right:

a which force, *X* or *Y*, has the greater turning effect on the nut? Explain your answer.

b how could the turning effect of force *Y* be increased?

4 In diagram **B** on the right, the plank is balanced:

a What is the moment of the 100N force about point O?

b What moment must the 400N force have to balance this?

c What is the distance of the 400N force from O?

5 Where would you expect the centre of mass of a metre ruler to be? How would you check this by experiment?

3.11 Pressure

Objectives

This spread should help you to
- calculate pressure
- describe how hydraulic machines work

Skis reduce the pressure on the snow by increasing the area which must support your weight.

same force

larger area

smaller area

lower pressure

higher pressure

You can't push your thumb into wood. But you can push a drawing pin in using the same force, because the force is concentrated on a much smaller area. Scientifically speaking, the **pressure** is higher.

Pressure is measured in **newtons per square metre** (N/m^2), also called **pascals** (Pa). It can be calculated with this equation:

$$pressure = \frac{force}{area}$$

force in newtons (N)
area in square metres (m^2)
pressure in pascals (Pa)

For example, if a force of 1200 N pushes (at right-angles) on an area of $4\,m^2$: pressure $= \dfrac{1200}{4} = 300\,N/m^2 = 300\,Pa$.

Liquid pressure

The deeper you go into a liquid, the greater the pressure becomes. This pressure pushes in all directions. It is the pressure from water which keeps a boat afloat. Water pressing on the hull produces an upward push called an **upthrust** which is strong enough to support the weight of the boat.

Questions

1 Why is it easier to walk on soft sand if you have flat shoes rather than shoes with small heels?

2 If a force of 12 N presses (at right-angles) on an area of $4\,m^2$, what is the pressure?

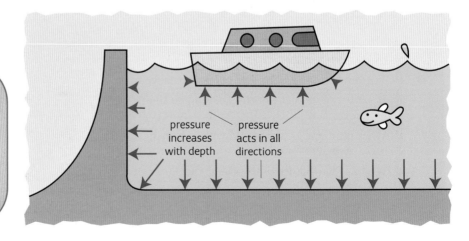

pressure increases with depth

pressure acts in all directions

Hydraulic machines

These are machines in which liquids are used to transmit forces. Machines like this rely on two features of liquids:

- Liquids cannot be squashed. They are virtually incompressible.
- If a trapped liquid is put under pressure, the pressure is transmitted throughout the liquid.

The diagram below shows a simple hydraulic jack. When you press on the narrow piston, the pressure is transmitted by the oil to the wide piston. It produces an output force which is larger than the input force. In other words, it is a **force magnifier**.

The shovel on this digger is moved hydraulically.

Follow the sequence of circled numbers 1–4 on the diagram. They show you how to use the link between pressure, force, and area to calculate the output force.

❶ input force 12 N

❷ pressure
$$= \frac{\text{force}}{\text{area}}$$
$$= \frac{12}{0.01}$$
$$= 1200\,\text{Pa}$$

area 0.01 m²

input cylinder

❸ pressure of 1200 Pa transmitted

area 0.1 m²

oil

output cylinder

❹ output force
= pressure × area
= 1200 × 0.1
= 120 N

Car brakes work hydraulically. When the brake pedal is pressed, a piston puts pressure on trapped brake fluid. The pressure is transmitted, by pipes, to the wheels. There, the pressure pushes on pistons which move the brake pads.

Questions

3 A rectangular block measures 4 m × 3 m × 2 m. It weighs 600 N and rests with one face on level ground. Draw a diagram to show the position of the block when the pressure under it is **a** as high as possible, **b** as low as possible.

Calculate the pressure in each case.

(Area of a rectangle = length × width)

4 In the simple hydraulic system on the right:

a what is the pressure of the oil?

b what is the output force?

c if the diameter of the output cylinder were greater, how would this affect the output force?

20 N input force

area 0.1 m²

oil

area 0.5 m²

output force

Stretching and compressing

Objectives

This spread should help you to

- describe how wires stretch
- describe how the pressure of a gas depends on its volume

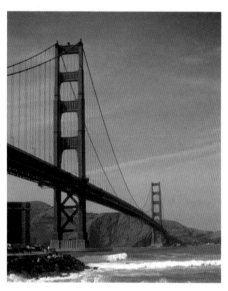

The steel cables on this bridge mustn't exceed their elastic limit.

Stretching a wire

When bridge-builders use steel cables, they need to know how much they will stretch and what load they can safely carry.

The experiment below shows the effect of a stretching force on a long, thin, steel wire. As the force increases, so does the **extension** (the length by which the cable stretches).

A graph of *extension* against *stretching force* is straight up to point X. Within this straight section:

- Each extra 100 N (newtons) of force produces the same extra extension (1 mm in this case).
- If the force doubles, the extension doubles, and so on.

If a material produces a straight-line graph like this, scientists say that it obeys **Hooke's law**. Steel and other metals obey Hooke's law. So do steel springs. But rubber and many plastics do not. With these materials, the graph would be a curve, not a straight line.

Point E on the graph is called the **elastic limit**. Up to this point, the cable will return to its original length if the force is removed. Scientifically speaking, the material is **elastic**. Beyond E, the cable becomes permanently stretched. At Y, it breaks. If a material does *not* return to its original shape when the stretching force is removed, then it is **inelastic**.

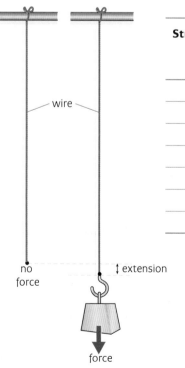

Stretching force in N	Extension in mm
0	0
100	1.0
200	2.0
300	3.0
400	4.0
500	5.6
600	–

Compressing a gas

If you squash a gas into a smaller volume, its pressure rises. The experiment below is designed to find out more about the link between pressure and volume. Some gas (air) is trapped in a cylinder. The gas is compressed by pushing in the piston, and the pressure and volume are measured at different stages.

Compressing the gas heats it up, which also affects the pressure. So the compression must be carried out very slowly so that the gas can lose heat and keep a steady temperature.

Volume in cm^3	50	40	25	20	10
Pressure in kPa	200	250	400	500	1000

The table gives some typical readings. They show that:

- If the volume is *halved,* the pressure is *doubled,* and so on.
- Pressure × volume keeps the same value (10 000 in this case).

These results are summed up by **Boyle's law**:

If a fixed mass of gas is kept at a steady temperature:

$$\text{original pressure} \times \text{original volume} = \text{final pressure} \times \text{final volume}$$

Questions

You will need graph paper for questions 2 and 3.

1 What is the difference between an *elastic* material and an *inelastic* one?

2 When a spring was stretched, these readings were taken:

Stretching force in N	0	1	2	3	4	5
Length in mm	40	49	58	67	79	99

a Make a table showing *stretching force* and *extension*.

b Plot a graph of *extension* against *stretching force*.

c How can you tell if the spring obeys Hooke's law?

d If it obeys this law, up to what point does it do so?

e What force produces an extension of 21 mm?

3 Look at the table above, giving volume and pressure readings for a trapped gas.

a Use the readings to plot a graph of *pressure* against *volume*.

b Describe what the graph shows.

c When the gas is at a pressure of 300 kPa, what is its volume?

4 A balloon contains 6 m³ of helium. As it rises through the atmosphere, the pressure falls from 100 kPa to 50 kPa, but the temperature stays the same. What is the new volume of the balloon?

Speedy delivery

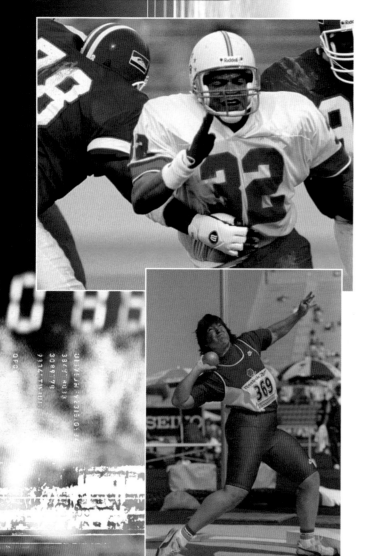

Making use of MASS

In American football, if your job is to charge through the defence lines, then you need as much mass as possible. The biggest players can have masses of over 120 kg. Once they start running, they are extremely difficult to stop.

The shot-putter below left needs mass as well as strength. When she pushes the shot forward, there is a backward push on her body which slows her down and reduces the speed of the shot. The more mass she has, the less effect this backward push has, and the better the throw.

Who wins over 1500 metres?

In a race like the one below, swimmers would lose out because water resistance is much higher than air resistance. Cyclists are fastest of all, and even faster if there is another vehicle in front to reduce the air resistance. The highest speed ever reached on a bicycle was 63 metres per second (140 m.p.h.) – behind a car with a windshield on the back.

1.5 m/s   7 m/s   12 m/s   15 m/s

30 m.p.h.

FAST SERVICE

Each image on this photograph was taken a fraction of a second after the previous one. Could you use the images to work out the speed of the racket? And if not, why not?

Getting the elbow

A top tennis player uses a tightly strung racket to help her serve fast. She tries to hit the ball near the centre of the racket. Otherwise, the forces can injure her elbow. An ordinary player uses strings that are less tight. The strings stretch more when the ball is hit, which cuts the speed down. But, if the player hits the ball off-centre, the forces on the elbow are small and not so damaging.

Talking points

Can you explain why:
● runners can travel faster than swimmers?
● cyclists can travel faster than runners?

See if you can find out how the following reduce the forces resisting their motion:

sprint cyclists   speed skaters   swimmers

Can you list the sports where having plenty of body mass is:

an advantage?   a disadvantage?

g and more g

On Earth, if you drop something, it accelerates downwards at 10 m/s² (assuming no air resistance). In other words, its speed increases by 10 m/s every second. This is called the **acceleration of free fall**, or *g*. It is the same number as the Earth's gravitational field strength, also called *g*.

g rides

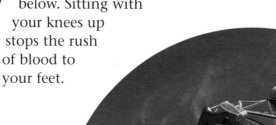

Leisure park rides like this one give you the effects of high acceleration by making you travel round tight bends very fast. The maximum acceleration is about 3*g*.

High acceleration can drain blood from your head to your feet and make you 'black out'. But not during the ride below. Sitting with your knees up stops the rush of blood to your feet.

For the 5*g* ride on the left, you need skill and a million pounds worth of training. You also need a special 'g-suit'. During tight turns, parts of it inflate to squeeze your limbs and abdomen, so that the drain of blood from your head is reduced.

The safest way to travel . . .

...is backwards, provided your seat has a high back.

Flying is already just about the safest form of travel there is. But if a plane has to make a crash landing, the deceleration can be very high. Rear-facing seats give the best chance of survival, which is why they are usually fitted in military transport aircraft. But so far, airlines haven't taken up the idea.

High *g* performers

Some animals have evolved an amazing ability to withstand high *g* values:

Squirrels have specially adapted front legs to absorb the shock of landing from great heights. Their deceleration can be 20*g* or more.

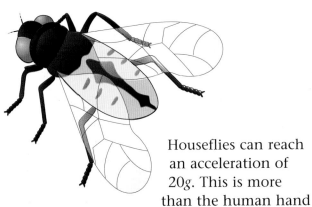

Houseflies can reach an acceleration of 20*g*. This is more than the human hand can produce, which is one reason why flies are so difficult to swat.

The click beetle can out-accelerate any other creature. It makes its escape by jack-knifing into the air with a peak acceleration of over 400*g*.

Talking points

— In leisure park rides, you can experience accelerations of 3*g* or more. But without head restraints, accelerations like this wouldn't be safe. Can you explain why not?

— By using this book or other sources of information, see if you can find out what safety features cars have to reduce the acceleration or deceleration that passengers experience in a crash.

— If rear-facing seats are safer, can you suggest reasons why no airline has decided to 'go it alone' and fit them?

1 The graph below describes the motion of a bus as it travels from village to village.

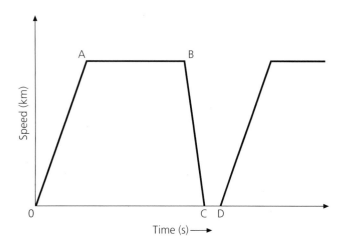

   i Describe in detail what is happening between OA, AB, BC and CD.

   ii Sketch an acceleration/time graph for the bus' journey.

2 Emma and Jane are having a race. The graph below shows how the speed of each athlete changes with time.

   a Which athlete reaches the higher speed?

   b Which athelete has the greater acceleration at the start of the race?

   c After how many seconds does Jane's speed become greater than Emma's?

   d What is Emma's maximum speed?

   e To begin with, Emma's acceleration is $2\,m/s^2$. What does this figure tell you about the way her speed changes?

3 The graph below shows a man's journey.

   a Calculate the man's average speed for the whole journey.

   b Calculate the man's speed in part A of the graph.

   c What is the man's speed in part B of the graph?

   d Calculate the man's speed in part C of the graph.

4 The table below shows how the stopping distance of a car depends on its speed.

Stopping distance (m)	0	4	12	22	36	52	72
Speed (m/s)	0	5	10	15	20	25	30

   a Write down TWO factors, apart from speed, that affect the stopping distance of a car.

   b Use the information in the above table to draw a graph of stopping distance against speed.

   c The speed limit in a housing estate is 12.5m/s.

      Use your graph to estimate the stopping distance of a car travelling at this speed.

   d Describe how the stopping distance changes as the speed of a car increases.

5 The diagram below shows a bobsleigh team at the beginning of their run.

a When the team push the bobsleigh the forces they apply cause it to accelerate. Name one place where the team need **i** a large amount of friction and **ii** as small amount of friction as possible.

b What do the team do on their way down the run to reduce any resistive forces?

c Why do the team need a lot of friction at the end of the run?

6 In each of the following cases, decide whether the frictional forces should be as *low* as possible or as *high* as possible:

a Shoes in contact with the pavement.

b Brake blocks being pressed against the rim of a bicycle wheel.

c Hands holding the handlebars of a bicycle.

d Skis sliding over snow.

e Car tyres in contact with a road surface.

f A wheel turning on its axle.

7 Copy and complete the following sentences.

a i When a stone is dropped it falls to the ground. The force causing this is called _____. As the stone falls its speed _____.

ii We measure forces in units called _____.

iii Before the stone was dropped it had _____ energy. Just before it hit the ground this had all changed into _____ energy.

b A crate weighing 1000 N is lifted a vertical distance of 2 m. Calculate the work done on the crate.

8 A lead ball and a feather are held at the same height above the ground and then released together.

a Which object hits the ground first? Explain your answer.

b Why do shuttlecraft which are returning from orbiting the Earth release 'drag chutes' just after they have landed?

9 a A car accelerates from 0 to 200 km/h in 20 s. What is the average acceleration of this car? Why is this *average* acceleration?

b A train slows down from 120 km/h to 40 km/h in 20 s. What is the deceleration of the train? What is the acceleration of the train?

c A small rocket on bonfire night accelerates from rest to 40 m/s in 4 s. What is the acceleration of the rocket?

10 A skydiver falls from a hovering helicopter. She waits a few seconds before opening her parachute. The table below shows how her speed changes with time from the moment she jumps:

Time (s)	0	1	2	3	4	5	6	7	8
Speed (m/s)	0		20	30	22	14	12	9	9

a Copy and complete the table, filling in the missing number.

b Plot a graph of speed against time.

c After how many seconds does the skydiver open her parachute? How can you tell from your graph?

d As the skydiver falls, there is a *downward* force acting on her and an *upward* force.

i What causes the downward force?

ii What causes the upward force?

iii After 2 seconds, which of these two forces is the larger?

iv After 8 seconds, how do the two forces compare?

e How would you expect your graph to be different if the skydiver's parachute were larger? (You could answer this by drawing sketches to show how the graph changes.)

11 The diagram below shows a model crane. The crane has a movable counterbalance.

a Why does the crane need a counterbalance?

b Why does the counterbalance need to be movable?

c In the diagram, what is the moment of the 100 N force about O?

d To balance the crane, what moment must the 400 N force have?

e How far from O should the counterbalance be positioned?

f Where would you expect the counterbalance to be positioned if the crane is lifting its maximum load?

g What is the maximum load the crane should lift?

h Describe two ways of making the design of the crane more stable.

12 Calculate the pressure exerted on the ground by

a a lady weighing 500 N if the total surface area of her stilleto heels in contact with the ground is 0.0025 m².

b an elephant weighing 5000 N if the total surface area of the soles of his feet is 0.1 m².

c a man weighing 750 N if the total surface area of his shoes in contact with the ground is 0.125 m².

13 The diagram below shows a drawing pin.

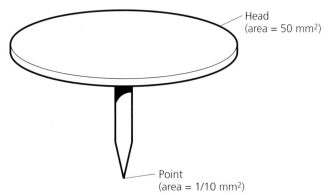

a A force of 50 N is applied to the head of the pin. Calculate the pressure in N/mm² created on the pin head.

b Calculate the pressure in N/mm² the 50 N force creates at the point of the pin.

14 A pupil carried out an experiment to prove Hooke's Law. Her results are shown in the table below.

Extension (mm)	0.3	0.6	0.9	1.2	1.7
Force (N)	1	2	3	4	5

a Draw a graph of the pupil's results.

b Does the graph confirm Hooke's Law? Explain your answer.

c What is likely to happen to this spring when the applied forces are removed?

15 The diagram below shows how a steel spring stretches when a weight is hung from it.

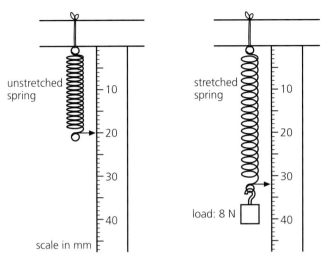

unstretched spring

scale in mm

stretched spring

load: 8 N

a What is the extension of the spring?

b If the spring obeys Hooke's Law, what does this tell you about the way the extension increases with load?

c What would you expect the extension to be for each of the following loads?

  i 4 N

  ii 6 N

d As more weights are added, the extension increases. How is the spring affected if it is taken past its elastic limit?

Key words

The spread numbers in brackets tell you where to find more information.

acceleration If the velocity of something increases by 10 m/s every second, then its acceleration is 10 m/s². *(3.01)*

force A push or pull. It is measured in newtons (N). *(3.04)*

friction The force that opposes the motion of one material over (or through) another. *(3.05, 3.08)*

gravitational field strength (of Earth), *g* Near the Earth's surface, this is 10 N/kg. In other words, there is a gravitational pull of 10 N on each kg of mass. *(3.04)*

moment The turning effect of a force. It is equal to the force × perpendicular distance to pivot (turning point). *(3.10)*

newton (N) Unit of force. *(3.04)*

retardation (deceleration) If the velocity of something decreases by 10 m/s every second, then the retardation is 10 m/s². *(3.01)*

speed If something travels a distance of 10 m in 1 second, its average speed is 10 m/s. *(3.01)*

velocity Speed in a particular direction. It is measured in m/s. An arrow, or a + or −, can be used to show its direction. *(3.01)*

weight The strength of the Earth's gravitational pull on an object. Being a force, it is measured in newtons (N). *(3.04)*

This hyla tree frog from South America uses the large, inflatable sac under its throat to amplify the sound of its voice. Only the males can do this, and their calls can travel ten times further than sounds from other frogs. The sound itself is generated when air from the sac is blown past two stretched membranes in the bottom of the frog's mouth, making them vibrate.

Moving waves

Objectives

This spread should help you to

- describe how waves travel
- understand the link between speed, frequency, and wavelength

If you drop a stone into a pond, tiny waves spread across the surface, as shown in the photograph above. The moving wave effect is the result of up-and-down motions in the water.

Light, sound, and radio signals all travel in the form of waves. Waves carry energy from one place to another, but without any material being transferred.

There are two main types of wave. You can demonstrate them with a 'slinky' spring as shown below. When a coil **oscillates** (moves to and fro), it makes the next one oscillate a fraction of a second later... and so on. This produces the moving wave effect.

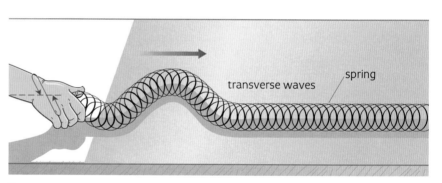

Transverse waves have oscillations which are from side to side (or up and down). Light and radio waves travel like this.

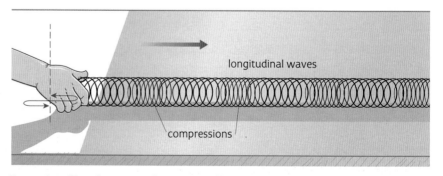

Longitudinal waves have oscillations which are backwards and forwards. Sound waves travel like this.

Did you know?

How to draw waves

Transverse waves can be drawn as shown above.

You can also draw waves using lines called wavefronts. Think of each wavefront as the top of a transverse wave, or the compression of a longitudinal wave.

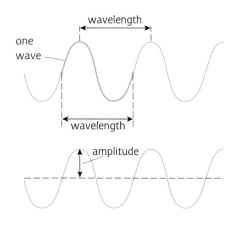

Describing waves

Imagine some waves travelling across water. Here are some of the terms used when describing them:

Speed This is measured in metres per second (m/s).

Frequency This is the number of waves sent out per second. It is measured in hertz (Hz). For example, if 3 waves are sent out every second, the frequency is 3 Hz.

Wavelength This is the distance from one point on a wave to the matching point on the next wave.

Amplitude This is the distance shown in the diagram .

Period This is the time between one wave peak and the next. For example, if 3 waves are sent out every second, the time between one wave peak and the next is $\frac{1}{3}$ second. So the period is $\frac{1}{3}$ second.

An equation for waves

Speed, frequency, and wavelength are linked by an equation. The panel below shows why it works:

speed	=	frequency	×	wavelength
in m/s		in Hz		in m

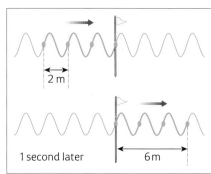

2 m

1 second later   6 m

3 waves pass the flag in one second...   ...so the frequency is 3 Hz.
Each wave is 2 metres long...   ...so the wavelength is 2 m.

This means that:

the waves travel 6 metres in one second...   ...so the speed is 6 m/s.

Therefore: 6 m/s   =   3 Hz   ×   2 m
                (speed)   (frequency)   (wavelength)

Questions

1 What is the difference between *longitudinal waves* and *transverse waves*?

2 Three waves have the *same speed*, but different frequencies and wavelengths. Copy the table to the right, and fill in the blank spaces.

	Speed in m/s	Frequency in Hz	Wavelength in m
wave 1		8	4
wave 2		16	
wave 3			1

Wave effects

You can use a **ripple tank** like the one above to study how waves behave. Ripples (tiny waves) are sent across the surface of the water, towards different obstacles. Here are some of the effects produced.

Reflection

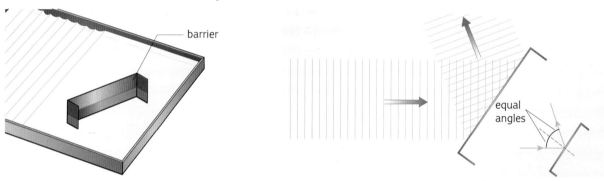

A vertical barrier is put in the path of the waves. The waves are reflected from the barrier at the same angle as they strike it.

Refraction

A flat piece of plastic makes the water more shallow. This slows the waves down. When they slow, they change direction. This bending effect is called **refraction**.

Diffraction

Waves bend round obstacles, or spread as they pass through gaps. This is called **diffraction**. It works best if the width of the gap is about the same as the wavelength. Wider gaps cause less diffraction.

Wave evidence

Sound, light, and radio signals can be reflected, refracted, and diffracted. This is evidence that they travel as waves. Sound waves diffract round large obstacles, which is why you can hear round corners. Light waves are much shorter, so gaps have to be very tiny to diffract them.

Questions

1 Write down whether each of the following is an example of *reflection*, *refraction*, or *diffraction*.

   a A beam of light bouncing off a mirror, as in photograph X on the right.

   b A beam of light bending on entering a glass block, as in photograph Y on the right.

   c Sound bending round a wall, so that you can hear someone speaking on the other side.

   d Radio waves bending round a hill, so that a radio can still pick up signals down in a valley.

2 In the diagram on the right, waves are moving towards a harbour wall.

   a What will happen to waves striking the harbour wall at A?

   b What will happen to waves slowed by the submerged sandbank at B?

   c What will happen to waves passing through the harbour entrance at C?

   d If the harbour entrance were wider, what difference would this make?

X   Y

Rays of light

Light is a form of radiation. This just means that light radiates (spreads out) from its source. In diagrams, lines called **rays** are used to show which way the light is going.

On Earth, the Sun is our main source of light.

If you can see a beam of light, this is because tiny particles of dust, smoke, or mist are reflecting some of the light into your eyes.

You see some things because they give off their own light. The Sun, lamps, lasers, and glowing TV screens are like this.

You see other things because daylight, or other light, bounces off them. They **reflect** light, and some goes into your eyes. That is why you can see this page. The white paper reflects light well, so it looks bright. However, the black letters **absorb** light and reflect very little. That is why they look so dark. Transparent materials like glass and water let light pass right through them. They **transmit** light.

Questions

1 Give *two* examples of things that give off their own light.

2 Give *two* examples of things that can only be seen because they reflect light from another source.

Irregular reflection

Regular reflection

Absorption

Transmission

Most surfaces are uneven, or contain materials that scatter light. They reflect light in all directions. In other words, the reflection is *irregular*. Mirrors are smooth and shiny. When they reflect light, the reflection is *regular*.

Light from a laser.

Features of light

Light travels in straight lines You can see this if you look at the path of a sunbeam or a laser beam.

Light travels as waves The 'ripples' can't be seen. They are tiny, vibrating electric and magnetic forces. The waves are transverse – their vibrations are the up-and-down type. They are also very small: more than 2000 light waves would fit into a millimetre.

To explain some effects, scientists find it useful to think of light as a stream of tiny 'energy particles'. They call them **photons**.

Light can travel through a vacuum (empty space) Electric and magnetic ripples do not need a material to travel through. That is why light can reach us from the Sun and stars.

Light is the fastest thing there is In space, the speed of light is 300 000 kilometres per second. Nothing can travel faster than this. The speed of light seems to be a universal speed limit.

Light delivers energy Energy is needed to produce light. Materials gain energy when they absorb light. For example, solar cells use the energy in sunlight to produce electricity.

This solar-powered car uses the energy in sunlight to produce electricity for its motor.

Questions

3 Which of the materials below would you expect to:
a mainly reflect light? **b** mainly absorb light?
c mainly transmit light?
(There may be more than one answer to each part.)

glass   aluminium   water   coal   snow

4 Give one piece of evidence that light waves can travel through a vacuum (empty space).

5 Give one piece of evidence that light delivers energy.

6 Give *two* pieces of evidence that light travels in straight lines.

7 Light is the fastest thing there is.
  a What is the speed of light? (You will find the information somewhere on this page.)
  b If the Moon is 384 000 km from Earth, will light from the Moon take *less* than one second to reach the Earth, or *more* than one second?

Reflections, rays, and waves

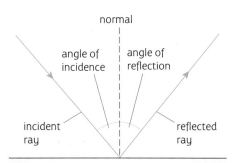

*How a mirror reflects light, and the terms used to describe the different rays and angles. (The line at right-angles to the mirror's surface is called a **normal**.)*

The windows of the building above act like a huge mirror. In this spread, you will find out what a mirror does to light, and why scientists think that light travels in the form of waves.

The diagram on the left shows what happens to a ray of light when it strikes a mirror. The light is reflected at the same angle as it arrives. Put scientifically:

The angle of incidence is equal to the angle of reflection.

Why you see an image in a mirror

Below, light rays are coming from a lamp in front of a mirror. Thousands of rays could have been drawn, but to keep things simple, only two have been shown. The rays are reflected into the girl's eye. To the girl, the rays seem to come from a position behind the mirror, so that is where she sees an **image** of the lamp.

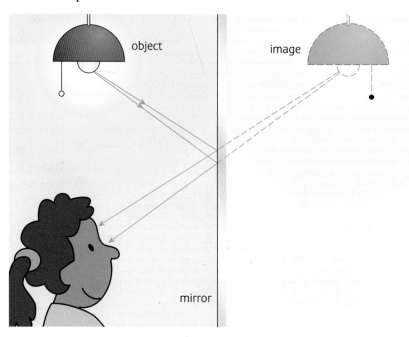

The girl sees an image of the lamp at a position where the reflected rays appear to come from.

Evidence for light waves

Waves bend round obstacles or spread through gaps – this is the effect called **diffraction**. When water waves pass through a gap, the diffraction is easy to see. The diffraction of light is usually much less obvious. However, the fact that it happens at all is evidence that light travels in the form of waves.

Here is a way of seeing the diffraction of light for yourself:

view without net curtain

view with net curtain

When it is dark, try looking out of a window, through a net curtain, at a distant street light. The net curtain needs to have a fine mesh. It also helps if you look through binoculars to magnify the effect. Instead of a single blob of light, you will see multiple images. These are formed by light waves as they diffract through the tiny holes in the curtain, and are bent off course.

red light

violet light

Wavelengths.

With any waves, if the size of the gap is very much bigger than the wavelength, the diffraction effect isn't enough to notice. Very small holes are needed to diffract light, which suggests that light waves have very short wavelengths. From the size of the gap and the amount of diffraction, scientists can calculate the wavelength of the waves. You can see some typical values for light waves on the left.

Questions

1 On the right, a ray of light strikes a mirror.

a The angle shown is 60°. What is this angle called?

b What is the angle of reflection in this case?

c Copy and complete the diagram, and label the *reflected ray* and the *angle of reflection*.

2 a Describe one piece of evidence that light travels in the form of waves.

b Why does this evidence suggest that light wavelengths are very short?

Bending light

In the 'broken pencil' illusion below left, the glass block bends the light as it enters and leaves it. The bending effect is called refraction. Water and other transparent materials also refract light, though by different amounts.

The 'broken pencil' illusion is caused by the refraction (bending) of light.

The diagram above shows how a ray passes through a glass block. The line at right-angles to the side of the block is called the **normal**. The ray is refracted towards the normal when it enters the block, and away from the normal when it leaves it.

With a rectangular block like the one above, the ray comes out parallel to its original direction. If the ray strikes the block at right-angles ('square on'), it goes straight through without being refracted.

Deeper than it looks

Because of refraction, water looks less deep than it really is. The diagram below shows why this happens.

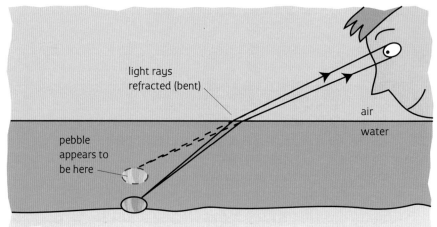

Questions

1 A glass block can bend light. What name is given to the bending effect?

2 In the photograph above, why does the middle of the pen appear to be moved to one side?

When rays from the pebble leave the water, they are refracted. To the viewer, they seem to come from a point that is higher, and closer. This effect makes objects look larger underwater. When scientists or archaeologists are working on marine life or wrecks, they tend to overestimate sizes and must measure for accuracy.

Forming a spectrum

Red light is refracted (bent) the least by a prism, and violet light the most. However, in this diagram, the difference has been exaggerated (it has been made to look bigger than it really is).

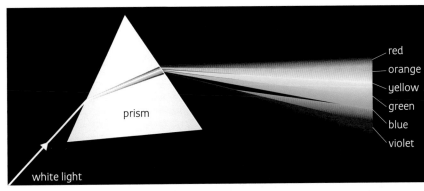

A **prism** is a triangular block of glass or plastic. When a narrow beam of white light passes through a prism, the beam splits into all the colours of the rainbow. That is because white isn't a single colour, but a mixture of colours. The colours enter the prism together but are refracted (bent) different amounts by the glass. The effect is called **dispersion**.

Raindrops can act like tiny prisms when sunlight strikes them.

The range of colours is called a **spectrum**. Most people think they can see six colours. However, the spectrum is really a continuous change of colour from beginning to end.

The different colours in the spectrum are actually light waves of different wavelengths. Red light has the longest wavelength, violet the shortest.

Questions

3 a Copy the diagram on the right. Draw in and label the *normal* and the *refracted ray*.

b Redraw the diagram to show what happens to a ray of light if it strikes the glass at right-angles ('square on').

4 When a narrow beam of white light passes through a prism, it spreads out into a range of colours.

a What is this range of colours called?

b Which colour is refracted (bent) most by a prism?

c Which colour is refracted least?

5 Why does water look less deep than it really is?

Internal reflections

This spread should help you to

- explain what total internal reflection is, and give some examples of its use

The inside surface of water, glass, or other transparent materials can act like a perfect mirror.

The diagrams below show what happens to three rays leaving an underwater lamp at different angles. If light strikes the surface at a angle greater than the **critical angle**, there is no refracted ray. All the light is reflected. The effect is called **total internal reflection**.

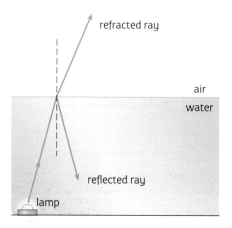

The ray splits into a refracted ray and a weaker reflected ray.

The ray splits, but the refracted ray only just leaves the surface.

There is no refracted ray. The surface of the water acts like a perfect mirror.

	Critical angles
water	49°
acrylic plastic	42°
glass	41°

The value of the critical angle depends on the material, as you can see in the table on the left.

Reflecting prisms

Total internal reflection can take place inside a prism. In the examples below, the prisms are made of glass or acrylic plastic.

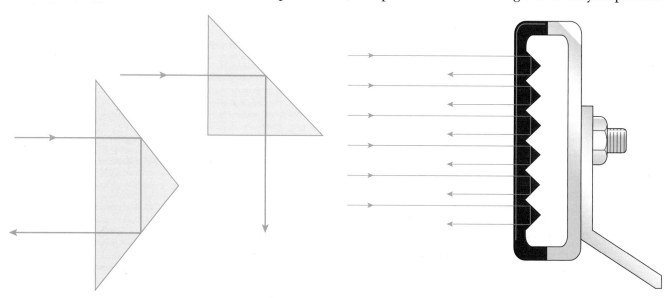

The inside faces of these prisms act like perfect mirrors because the light is striking them at 45°. That is bigger than the critical angle for glass or acrylic plastic.

The rear reflectors on cars and cycles contain lots of tiny prisms. These use total internal reflection to send light back in the opposite direction.

Optical fibres

Optical fibres are very thin, flexible rods of glass (or transparent plastic). They use total internal reflection. Light put in at one end is reflected from side to side until it comes out of the other end, as shown below.

A single optical fibre. In the type shown here, the core has a coating around it to protect its reflecting surface.

A bundle of optical fibres. If the fibres are in matching positions at both ends, you can see a picture through them.

A group of optical fibres. Telephone calls can be carried by optical fibres. The signals are coded and sent along the fibre as pulses of laser light.

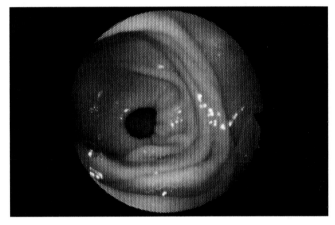

*This photograph was taken through an **endoscope**, an instrument used by surgeons for looking inside the body. An endoscope contains a long, thin bundle of optical fibres.*

Questions

1 Copy and complete the diagrams right to show where each ray goes after it strikes the prism.

2 When light goes into one end of an optical fibre, why does it all come out of the other end, with none escaping from the sides?

3 **a** Give *two* examples of the practical use of optical fibres.

   b Give one more example of the practical use of total internal reflection.

4 Glass's critical angle is 41°. What does this mean?

Electromagnetic waves

radio waves

| long waves | medium waves | short waves | VHF | UHF | microwaves |

1000 m   1 m   1 mm

very long

The different types of electromagnetic wave. They are sometimes called electromagnetic radiation because they radiate (spread out) from their source.

A microwave aerial for satellite TV.

A hot, glowing material like this is giving off a mixture of visible red light and invisible infrared.

Light is a member of a whole family of waves called the **electromagnetic spectrum**.

Radio waves These are produced by making a current vibrate in an aerial. They can be sent out in a special pattern which tells a radio or TV what sounds or pictures to make.

Long and medium waves are used for AM radio.

VHF (very high frequency) waves are used for high-quality FM stereo radio.

UHF (ultra high frequency) waves are used for terrestrial TV.

Microwaves These are radio waves of very short wavelength. They are used for satellite communication, beaming television and telephone signals round the country, and mobile phone networks. They are also used for radar.

Some microwaves are absorbed strongly by food. Their energy makes the food hot. Microwave ovens make use of this idea.

Infrared Hot things like fires all give off infrared radiation. In fact, everything gives off some infrared. If you absorb it, it heats you up.

As objects get hotter, the infrared wavelengths they give off get shorter. When something is 'red hot', some wavelengths are so short that they can be picked up by the eye.

TV remote controllers send instructions using infrared pulses.

Light This is the only part of the spectrum which the eye can detect.

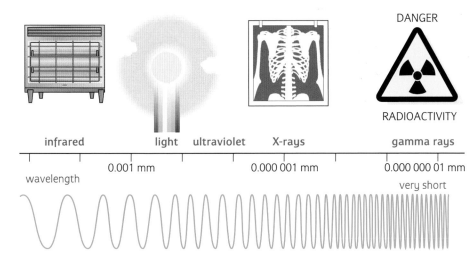

infrared   light ultraviolet X-rays   gamma rays

DANGER

RADIOACTIVITY

Features of electromagnetic waves
- *They carry energy.*
- *They can travel through empty space.*
- *Their speed through space (and air) is 300 000 km/s. This is called the* **speed of light***, although they all travel at this speed.*

wavelength   0.001 mm   0.000 001 mm   0.000 000 01 mm   very short

The Sun's ultraviolet radiation causes tanning – and skin cancer.

Ultraviolet This is present in sunlight, although your eyes can't detect it. It is the type of radiation that produces a sun tan. But too much can cause skin cancer, and damage your eyes.

Some chemicals glow when they absorb ultraviolet. The effect is called **fluorescence**. In fluorescent lamps, the inside of the tube is coated with a white powder which glows and gives off light when it absorbs ultraviolet from 'electrified' gas in the tube.

X-rays Shorter wavelengths can penetrate dense metals. Longer wavelengths can pass through flesh, but not bone. So they can be used to take 'shadow' photographs of bones. Only brief bursts are allowed because X-rays can damage living cells and cause cancer.

Gamma rays These come from radioactive materials and have the same effects as X-rays. They can be used for sterilizing medical instruments, because they kill germs. Concentrated beams of gamma rays (or X-rays) can be used to kill cancer cells.

Questions

1 The chart at the top of the page shows the different types of electromagnetic wave. Give *two* features that all the waves in the chart have.

2 Write down which of the electromagnetic waves are described by each of the following (in some cases, there may be more than one type):

   a can be detected by the eye.

   b can pass right through flesh.

   c have the longest wavelength.

   d are used for radar.

   e are given off by warm objects.

   f are given off by red-hot objects.

   g are used for cooking.

   h cause sun-tanning in some types of skin.

   i can damage living cells deep in the body.

   j are sent out in pulses by TV remote controllers.

   k are used for communications.

   l cause chemicals to glow in fluorescent lamps.

Sending signals

Objectives

This spread should help you to

- explain how information can be sent using wires, optical fibres, or radio waves
- describe how analogue and digital signals differ

Telephone, radio, and TV are all forms of **telecommunication** – ways of transmitting (sending) information over long distances. The information may be sounds, pictures, or computer data.

In the simple telephone system above, the microphone turns the incoming information (speech) into a changing electric current. The changes, called **signals**, pass along wires to the earphone. This turns them back into useful information (speech). In a real system, **amplifiers** are used to boost the strength of the signals.

Analogue and digital signals

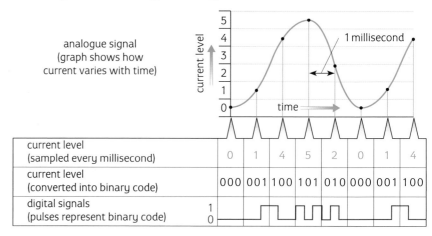

How an analogue signal is converted into digital pulses. Real systems use hundreds of levels and a faster sampling rate.

The sound waves entering a microphone make the current through it vary – as shown above. A continuous variation like this is called an **analogue signal**. The table shows how it can be converted into **digital signals** – signals represented by numbers. The current is **sampled** (measured) electronically many times per second, and the measurements changed into **binary codes** (numbers using only 0s and 1s). These are transmitted as a series of pulses and turned back into analogue signals at the receiving end.

Questions

1 What is the difference between an *analogue* signal and a *digital* signal?

2 What does an *amplifier* do?

Optical fibres from inside a cable. Cables like this need fewer booster stations than electrical cables.

Advantages of digital transmission

Digital signals have two main advantages over analogue ones:

- Digital signals reach the receiving end unchanged. Analogue signals lose quality during transmission.
- Digital signals can carry more information along a cable (or radio channel) than analogue signals can.

Using optical fibres

Optical fibres are thin, flexible strands of glass or plastic. Digital signals can be sent along them as pulses of infrared or light. Optical fibre cables are thinner and lighter than electric cables. They can carry more signals, with less loss of power. Telephone networks use them for long-distance transmission.

Using radio waves

Radio waves are used for TV and mobile phones, as well as radio. Sent from a **transmitter**, they generate a tiny current in the aerial of the **receiver**. To carry the signals, a set of waves called the **carrier** must be varied in some way. With **AM** (**amplitude modulation**), the strength is varied, with **FM** (**frequency modulation**), the frequency is varied. FM is less affected by interference.

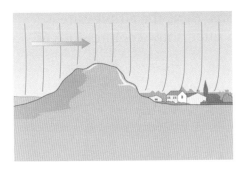

Long and medium waves diffract (bend) round hills.

Long and medium waves will diffract (bend) round hills. Some are also reflected by the **ionosphere** – a layer of charged particles in the upper atmosphere. This increases their range. Higher frequencies need a straight route to an aerial.

Typical radio frequencies				
1 kilohertz (kHz) = 1000 waves per second		1 megahertz (MHz) = 1000 000 waves per second		
AM radio long wave 200 kHz	AM radio medium wave 1 MHz	FM radio VHF 100 MHz	television UHF 500 MHz	mobile phone 900 MHz

Questions

3 Telephone systems sometimes make use of optical fibres.

   a In what form do the signals travel along the fibre?

   b Give *two* advantages of sending digital signals rather than analogue ones.

   c Give *two* advantages of using an optical fibre link rather than a cable with wires in it.

4 Explain why, in a valley, long-wave AM reception may be good, but VHF reception poor.

5 a What do FM and AM stand for?

   b Give one advantage of sending radio signals using FM rather than AM.

6 A radio station broadcasts on a frequency of 2 MHz.

   a How many radio waves is the station's transmitting aerial sending out every second?

   b What is the frequency in Hz?

   c What is the frequency in kHz?

Sound waves

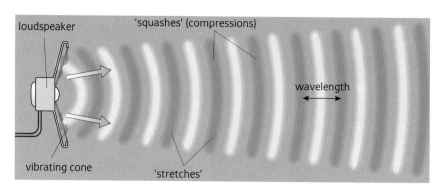

When the cone of a loudspeaker vibrates, it moves in and out very fast, stretching and squashing the air in front of it. The 'stretches' and 'squashes' spread through the air – rather as ripples spread across a pond. They are **sound waves**. When they reach your ears, they make your eardrums vibrate and you hear a **sound**.

The 'squashes' are **compressions**. Here, the air pressure is higher than normal. Diagrams often show compressions as lines.

Features of sound

Sound waves are caused by vibrations Any vibrating object can be a source of sound waves. The cone of a loudspeaker is one example. There are some more above.

Sound waves are longitudinal waves This means that their vibrations are backwards and forwards, rather than up and down like ripples.

Sound waves can be reflected and refracted There is more about this in the next spread.

Sound waves can be diffracted This means that they can bend round obstacles and through gaps. That is why you can hear round corners.

Questions

1 In sound waves, what is the distance between compressions called?

2 How are sound waves different from the ripples that spread across water?

glass jar

rubber bands

electric bell

air removed

battery

← vacuum pump

If the air is removed from the jar, the bell can't be heard.

Sound waves can travel through solids, liquids, and gases
Most sounds reaching the ear have travelled through air. But you also hear sounds underwater. Walls, windows, doors, and ceilings can also transmit (pass on) sound.

Sound waves can't travel through a vacuum (empty space)
If the air is pumped out of the jar on the left, the sound stops, though the bell goes on working. Sound waves can't be made if there's no material to squash and stretch.

Seeing sounds

You can't actually see sounds. But with an **oscilloscope** connected to a **microphone**, you can show sounds as wave shapes on a screen.

oscilloscope (CRO)

sound waves

microphone

Did you know?

The waveform on the right looks like a series of waves. But it is really a graph of pressure against time. It shows how the air pressure near the microphone rises and falls as sound waves pass.

When sound waves go into the microphone, the vibrations are changed into electrical signals. The oscilloscope uses these to make a spot vibrate up and down on the screen. It moves it steadily sideways at the same time. The result is called a **waveform**.

Questions

3   *compressions*   *vibrations*   *waveforms*
Choose the word above which goes with each of the following:

a Sound waves are caused by these.

b In sound waves, these are regions of higher pressure.

4 Give one piece of evidence that shows each of the following:

a Sound can travel through a gas.

b Sound can travel through a liquid.

c Sound can travel through a solid.

d Sound cannot travel through a vacuum.

5 Give a reason for each of the following:

a Sound cannot travel through a vacuum.

b It is possible to hear round corners.

6 Sound waves are longitudinal waves – their vibrations are backwards-and-forwards. Why are transverse (up-and-down) 'waves' seen on the screen of the oscilloscope when someone whistles into the microphone?

Speed of sound and echoes

Objectives

This spread should help you to
- describe how fast sound travels
- explain how echoes are produced

Sound is much slower than light, so you hear lightning after you see it.

Speed of sound in ...

air at 0°C	330 m/s
air at 30°C	350 m/s
water at 0°C	1400 m/s
concrete	5000 m/s

The speed of sound

In air, the speed of sound is about 330 metres per second (760 m.p.h.), although this can vary depending on the temperature.

Sound takes about 3 seconds to travel one kilometre. Light does it almost in an instant. So, if you see lightning, then hear the crash 3 seconds later, the lightning must be about a kilometre away.

Sound travels faster in liquids than in gases (such as air). It travels fastest of all in solids. There are some examples on the left.

Refraction of sound

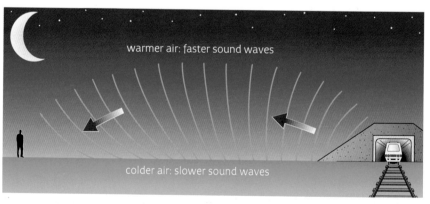

warmer air: faster sound waves

colder air: slower sound waves

Distant trains and traffic often sound louder at night. During the night-time, when the ground cools quickly, air near the ground becomes colder than that above. Sound waves travel more slowly through this colder air. So waves leaving the ground tend to bend back towards it, instead of spreading upwards. The bending effect is called **refraction**.

Questions

1 Why do you hear lightning after you see it?

2 If their speed changes, sound waves may change direction. What is this effect called?

Reflection of sound: echoes

Hard surfaces such as walls reflect sound waves. When you hear an **echo**, you are hearing a reflected sound a short time after the original sound.

echo time 0.5 s

80 m

Above, the girl is 80 metres from a large brick wall. Every time she hits the block of wood, she hears an echo 0.5 seconds later. This is the echo time. It is the time taken for the sound to travel the 160 metres to the wall *and back again*.

Now you can work out a value for the speed of sound:

$$\text{speed of sound} = \frac{\text{distance travelled}}{\text{time taken}} = \frac{\text{distance to wall and back}}{\text{echo time}}$$

So:

$$\text{speed of sound} = \frac{160}{0.5} = 320 \text{ metres/second (m/s)}$$

If you measure an echo time, but already know the speed of sound, you can work out how far away the reflecting surface is. This is the idea behind the **echo-sounders** which ships use to measure depth. You can find out more about them in the spread on **Ultrasound**.

Questions

Assume that the speed of sound in air is 330 m/s.

3 Which of the things in the chart below is travelling faster than sound does in air?

Time taken to travel 1000 metres		
racing car		5 seconds
jet plane		2 seconds
bullet		4 seconds

4 If lightning strikes, and you hear it 4 seconds after you see it, how far away is it?

5 Which does sound travel faster through:
 a *cold air* or *warm air*?
 b *a solid* or *a gas*?

6 A ship is 330 metres from a large cliff when it sounds its foghorn.
 a When the echo is heard on the ship, how far has the sound travelled?
 b What is the echo time (the time delay before the echo is heard)?

4.11 High and low, loud and quiet

Objectives

This spread should help you to

• describe how high sounds differ from low ones, and loud sounds from quiet ones

• use the wave equation

He sings louder than her. He creates bigger vibrations in the air. But she can reach higher notes than him. She can give out more sound waves every second.

Frequency and pitch

The **frequency** of a sound is measured in hertz (Hz). If a loudspeaker cone vibrates 100 times per second, it gives out 100 sound waves per second, and the frequency is 100 Hz.

Different frequencies sound different to the ear. You hear *high* frequencies as *high* notes: they have a **high pitch**. You hear *low* frequencies as *low* notes: they have a **low pitch**. So:

The higher the frequency of a sound, the higher its pitch.

The human ear can detect frequencies ranging from about 20 Hz up to 20 000 Hz, although the upper limit gets less with age.

Below, you can see what different frequencies look like on the screen of an oscilloscope. With the higher frequency, there are more waves on the screen: the waves are closer together.

Frequency		Pitch
20 000 Hz	highest frequency heard (human ear)	high
10 000 Hz	whistle	
1000 Hz	high note from singer	
100 Hz	low note from singer	
20 Hz	drum	low

waveform

This sound has a higher pitch (and frequency) ...   ... than this sound.

108

Amplitude and loudness

This sound is louder...   ... than this sound.

*Low **and** loud.*

The sounds shown on the oscilloscope screens above have the same frequency. But one is *louder* than the other. The vibrations in the air are bigger and the **amplitude** of the waveform is greater. So:

> The greater the amplitude, the louder the sound is.

The wave equation

This equation applies to sound waves, just like other waves:

speed	=	frequency	×	wavelength
in m/s		in Hz		in m

The higher the frequency, the shorter the wavelength.

Wave examples

The speed of sound in air is 330 m/s. From the equation on the right:
sound waves of frequency 110 Hz have a wavelength of 3 m.
Sound waves of frequency 330 Hz have a wavelength of 1 m.

Questions

1 Sound A: 400 Hz   Sound B: 200 Hz

Sounds A and B are played equally loudly. For someone listening to the two sounds, how would B compare with A?

2 A microphone picks up three different sounds, **X**, **Y**, and **Z**, one after another. On the right, you can see their waveforms on the screen of an oscilloscope.

  a Which sound has the greatest amplitude?

  b Which sound is the loudest?

  c Which sound has the highest frequency?

  d Which sound has the highest pitch?

3 In question **1**, which of the two sounds, A or B, has the longer wavelength?

4 Use the wave equation on this page to work out the wavelength of a sound whose frequency is 660 Hz. (Assume that the speed of sound in air is 330 m/s.)

X   Y   Z

Ultrasound

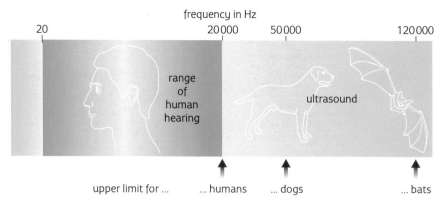

frequency in Hz

20   20000   50000   120000

range of human hearing

ultrasound

upper limit for ...   ... humans   ... dogs   ... bats

The human ear can detect sounds up to a frequency of about 20000 Hz. Sounds above the range of human hearing are called **ultrasonic sounds**, or **ultrasound**. Here are some of the uses of ultrasound:

Cleaning and breaking

Using ultrasound, delicate machinery can be cleaned without taking it to bits. The machinery is put in a tank of liquid. Then the vibrations of high-power ultrasound are used to shift the bits of dirt and grease.

In hospitals, concentrated beams of ultrasound can break up kidney stones and gall stones without patients needing surgery.

Echo-sounding

Ships use **echo-sounders** to measure the depth of water beneath them. An echo-sounder sends pulses of ultrasound downwards towards the seabed, as shown on the left. Then it measures the time taken for each echo (reflected sound) to return. The longer the time, the deeper the water.

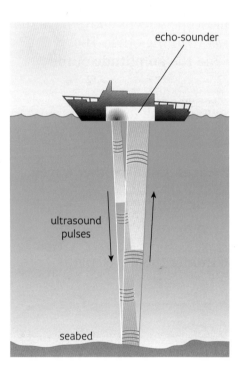

echo-sounder

ultrasound pulses

seabed

A ship uses an echo-sounder to measure the depth of the water.

Questions

1 What is *ultrasound*?
2 What is an *echo-sounder* used for?
3 How does an echo-sounder work?

This bat uses ultrasound to find insects and other things in front of it. It sends out ultrasound pulses and uses its specially shaped ears to pick up the reflections.

pulse sent out

pulse reflected from flaw

pulse reflected from end

oscilloscope

time

ultrasound transmitter/ detector

metal under test

flaw

end

Using ultrasound to test a metal for flaws.

Metal testing

Flaws in metals can be detected using the echo-sounding idea. A pulse of ultrasound is sent through the metal, as on the left. If there is a flaw (tiny gap) in the metal, *two* pulses are reflected back to the detector – one from the flaw and the other from the far end of the metal. The pulses can be displayed using an oscilloscope.

Scanning the womb

The pregnant mother below is having her womb scanned by ultrasound. A transmitter sends pulses of ultrasound into the mother's body. A detector picks up pulses reflected from the baby and different layers inside the body. The signals are processed by a computer, which puts an image on the screen.

'Seeing' inside the womb with ultrasound is much safer than using X-rays, because X-rays can cause cell damage in a growing baby.

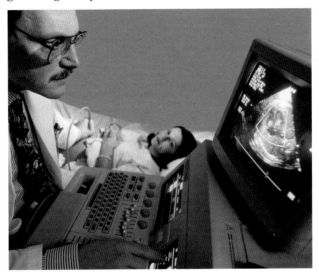

An ultrasound scan of the womb. The doctor is moving an ultrasound transmitter/ detector over the mother's body. A computer uses the reflected pulses to produce an image.

Questions

4 In hospitals, doctors can use ultrasound to 'see' into a pregnant mother's womb.

  a Why do doctors prefer to use ultrasound for this, rather than X-rays?

  b Give one other use of ultrasound in hospitals.

5 Give *two* uses of ultrasound in industry.

6 To answer this question, you will need the information on the right.

  A boat is fitted with an echo-sounder which uses ultrasound with a frequency of 40 kHz.

  a What is the frequency of the ultrasound in Hz?

  b If an ultrasound pulse takes 0.1 seconds to travel from the boat to the seabed and back, how far does it travel?

  c How deep is the water under the boat?

> speed of sound in water = 1400 metres per second (m/s)
>
> 1 kilohertz (kHz) = 1000 Hz
>
> $$\text{speed} = \frac{\text{distance travelled}}{\text{time taken}}$$

4.13 Seismic waves

Objectives

This spread should help you to

• explain where seismic waves come from
• describe the Earth's inner structure

Earthquake damage.

The photograph above shows the damage done by an earthquake. Earthquakes are caused by sudden rock movements underground. The vibrations send **seismic waves** (shockwaves) through the Earth.

Seismic waves get weaker as they travel through the ground. However, many thousands of kilometres away, they can be detected and recorded by a sensitive instrument called a **seismograph**. A simple type is shown below. Any small vibrations in the ground are magnified so that a pen moves up and down. The pen draws a graph on a slowly revolving drum.

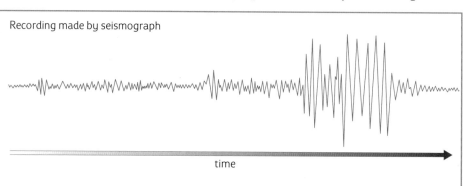

Clues from underground

By studying graphs from recording stations in different places, scientists can work out where the earthquake was, how strong it was, and what kinds of rock the seismic waves travelled through.

Geologists working for oil companies sometimes use small explosions to send shockwaves into the ground. By detecting the waves reflected from different rock layers, they can work out whether there is likely to be any oil in the rocks.

Questions

1 What causes seismic waves?
2 What instrument is used to detect seismic waves?

Inside the Earth

By studying seismic waves, scientists have built up a picture of what the Earth is like inside. There are three main zones:

The **crust** is the Earth's thin outer layer. The continents are the thickest part (up to 90 km). The rock here is mainly **granite**. Under the oceans, the crust is thinner and mainly **basalt**.

The **mantle** is mostly solid rock, made of **silicates**. However, the heat and pressure keep it flexible, rather like Plasticine. This means that it can flow. Heat from deep in the Earth makes it circulate very slowly.

The **core** is mostly molten (melted) iron, though the inner core is kept solid by the great pressure there. This is the hottest part of the Earth. Deep in the core, the temperature reaches 5000°C.

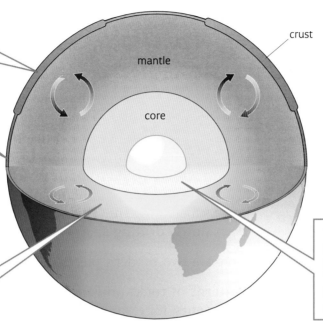

Density of the Earth

At the Earth's surface, the rocks have an average density of 2800 kg/m^3. In other words, they have 2800 kilograms of mass packed into every cubic metre. However, from the strength of the Earth's gravity, scientists know that the average density of the *whole* Earth must be much higher: 5500 kg/m^3.

If rocks at the surface are *less* dense than the average for the whole Earth, then the materials deep in the Earth must be *more* dense. That is one of the reasons why scientists think that the Earth's core is mainly iron.

Questions

3 The diagram on the right shows a simplified section through the Earth. Which of the zones, **X**, **Y**, or **Z**, goes with each of the following?

a the core

b the crust

c the mantle

d flexible enough to flow very slowly

e the hottest zone

f mostly molten iron

g made of the least dense materials

Moving continents (1)

Objectives

This spread should help you to

- give some evidence that the continents are moving
- describe what plates are, and how they are linked with earthquakes

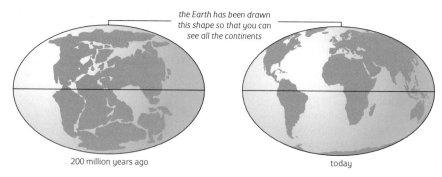

the Earth has been drawn this shape so that you can see all the continents

200 million years ago

today

Africa

South America

Mid-Atlantic ridge

Atlantic ocean

Key:

⟵ ⟶ direction of sea-floor spreading

very old rocks

In 1915, Alfred Wegener pointed out that the shapes of the continents could fit together like the pieces of a giant jigsaw. In his theory of **continental drift**, he suggested that the continents are like huge rafts which 'float' on the denser material underneath. Millions of years ago, there was one huge supercontinent. This split into pieces, and these have been slowly drifting apart ever since.

Here are two modern pieces of evidence to support this idea:

Patterns of rocks and fossils These match on different continents: for example, along the Atlantic coasts of Africa and South America.

Sea-floor spreading Molten (melted) rock is oozing out of volcanic cracks in a ridge running along the bottom of the Atlantic Ocean. It is cooling, and solidifying to form new crust. As it does so, the Atlantic is slowly getting wider – by a few centimetres a year.

Plates

Scientists now think that the Earth's crust (and upper mantle) is divided up into large sections, called **plates**. These are slowly moving over the denser, more flexible material beneath them.

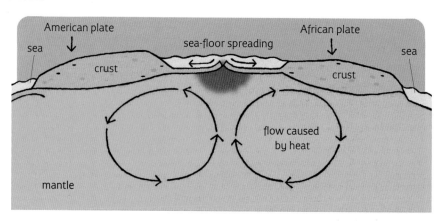

American plate   sea-floor spreading   African plate

sea   ↓   ↓   sea

crust   crust

flow caused by heat

mantle

Africa and America are slowly moving apart because of a flow of material in the mantle.

Earthquakes and volcanoes

• = earthquake site

Lava flowing from a volcano.

Where plates slide or push against against each other, there may be earthquakes. On the map above, each red dot shows where an earthquake has happened in the last 20 years. Together, the red dots show where the different plates meet.

Most volcanoes are near plate edges, where the crust is cracked and weak. These are also the places where the friction of plates rubbing together can produce heat. Hot rock in the mantle turns liquid and is pushed out from volcanoes as **lava**.

Why plates move

Most of the rock in the mantle is hot but not molten. However, it is flexible enough to flow very slowly, and it does so because of the effect of heat. The heat comes from radioactive materials which are naturally present in the Earth, and it causes **convection currents** in the mantle. (A convection current is a circulating flow of material caused by heat. For example, the hotplate on a cooker causes convection currents in the water in a saucepan.)

Questions

1 In 1915, Alfred Wegener suggested that, millions of years ago, the continents may all have been part of one huge supercontinent. What observation did he make that gave him this idea?

2 Give *two* pieces of evidence to support the idea that the continents have moved apart.

3 What do scientists mean by *plates*?

4 The map at the top of the page shows the sites of earthquakes over the last twenty years.

   a Explain why earthquakes tend to happen along the lines shown, rather than all over the Earth.

   b Explain why volcanoes also tend to be found close to the lines marked by the red dots.

5 What causes the slow movements of the Earth's plates?

Moving continents (2)

Objectives

This spread should help you to

- describe what happens at plate boundaries
- explain how rocks are recycled

The theory of plates and their movements is called **plate tectonics**. Plates meet at boundaries. There are three main types of boundary:

Constructive boundaries These are mainly under oceans. Plates move apart and grow as molten rock oozes up through cracks and cools to form new crust. The molten rock is called **magma**.

Destructive boundaries Plates move together so that one is **subducted** (carried down) under the other. Heat from the friction may melt the rock, causing volcanoes where magma is pushed out of the ground as lava. And as the plates collide, layers of rock are crumpled into **folds**, forming mountains.

Conservative boundaries Plates slide past each other, so their shape is 'conserved' – it does not change. Sometimes, the plates catch on each other. When they jerk free, there may be big earthquakes.

New rocks from old

Over millions of years, rocks in the crust can be subducted, melt to form magma, be uplifted, and then solidify to form new rock. The recycling of old rock to form new is called the **rock cycle**.

Folded rocks.

Rock crystals magnified

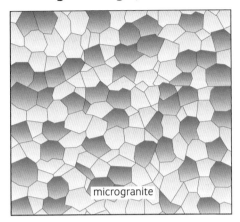

microgranite

This rock cooled more quickly...

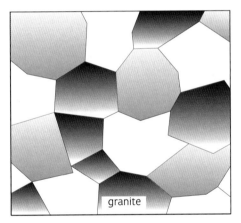

granite

...than this rock.

There are three main types of rock in the Earth's crust:

Igneous rocks, such as granite and basalt, are made of tiny crystals. They are formed when magma cools and solidifies.

If magma cools *quickly*, the crystals are *small*. This happens, for example, when lava comes out of a volcano and cools. If magma cools *slowly*, the crystals have time to grow, and are *large*. This can happens to magma deep in the crust.

Sedimentary rocks, such as sandstone and limestone, are formed from layers of sediment dropped by water or wind. In many cases, the sediment is bits worn away from old rock. As more sediment collects above it, it gets compressed, and sets like concrete.

Metamorphic rocks Deep underground, igneous and sedimentary rocks can be recrystallized by heat or pressure or both. They become metamorphic ('changed') rock which is usually harder than the original. Examples include marble and slate.

Questions

1 What is *magma*?

2 Here are two ways in which plates may move:

towards each other   *away from each other*

   a Which of the above produces fold mountains?

   b Which of the above produces a subduction zone?

   c In what other way can plates move?

3 Why may volcanoes form above a subduction zone?

4 Why are metamorphic rocks likely to be found near a subduction zone?

5 Igneous rock is formed when magma cools. How could you tell, by looking at the rock, whether the magma had cooled quickly or slowly?

The human ear can hear frequencies ranging from about 20 Hz (20 sound waves per second) up to about 20 000 Hz. Within that range, sounds can be varied and mixed to produce the complicated patterns we call music.

Changing Note

The higher the frequency of the sound waves, the higher the pitch of the note you hear.

On a guitar, you raise the pitch of a note by pressing the string against a fret to shorten the length that can vibrate. During tuning, you tighten or slacken the string to adjust the pitch.

On a trombone, you can raise the pitch of a note by shortening the length of tubing that the sound waves travel along. You can also change pitch by controlling how your lips vibrate when you blow.

Steel bands use tuned oil drums called **pans**. The end of each pan is skilfully shaped so that different sections produce different notes when hit.

1 octave	1 octave	1 octave	1 octave

middle C

| 64 Hz | 128 Hz | — frequency — | 256 Hz | 512 Hz | 1024 Hz |

Octaves

Musical scales are based on **octaves**. If two notes are an octave apart, one has *double* the frequency of the other. (The keyboard above is tuned to 'scientific pitch'. Bands and orchestras tune to slightly different frequencies.)

The Same but Different

If you play Middle C on a guitar, it doesn't sound quite the same as Middle C on a piano. Each sound has a strong **fundamental frequency**, giving Middle C. But other, weaker frequencies, called **overtones**, are mixed in. These differ from one type of instrument to another.

An electronic keyboard or synthesizer has a built-in computer which can mix different frequencies to produce the sound of a guitar, piano, or any other instrument. To sound right, each note must begin and end correctly. For example, the 'plonk' of a piano starts suddenly and then fades away: it has a short **attack** and a longer **decay**. The synthesizer must produce this effect as well.

Talking points

By using information from this spread or elsewhere, can you explain why:

🎼 a guitar string produces a higher note if you tighten it?

🎼 a guitar doesn't sound like a saxophone, even if both play the same note?

🎼 an electronic synthesizer can reproduce the sound of almost any musical instrument?

Radio waves from space

Stars, such as the Sun, give off light. But they give off other forms of radiation as well, including radio waves. **Radio telescopes** like those below pick up these waves. In space, radio signals can travel through clouds of dust that block light, so radio telescopes can 'see' stars that might be invisible through an ordinary telescope.

The image of distant stars on the left was created by a computer, using signals from a radio telescope. The colours are false.

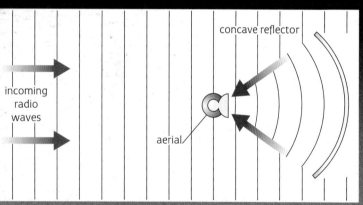

The main feature of most radio telescopes is a huge concave (dish-shaped) reflector. This focuses the radiation onto a tiny aerial. The dish needs to be large for two reasons. First, a large collecting area means that the faintest and most distant stars can be detected. Second, when incoming waves meet the dish, there is less diffraction. Any diffraction blurs the final image.

Building large dishes is difficult and expensive. An easier solution is to use an array of smaller dishes, as below, and combine the signals.

Gamma fresh

These strawberries were picked three weeks before the photograph was taken.

So were the ones below, but these were put straight into a beam of gamma radiation. The radiation stopped the rotting process, so old strawberries look as fresh as the day they were picked.

Irradiating fruit could mean better quality, less waste, and lower prices. Although the radiation doesn't make the fruit radioactive, critics say that it may destroy vitamins and affect substances in the fruit. And when you next buy fresh strawberries, how fresh will they really be?

Ultra-bright

The Sun's rays include some ultraviolet radiation. Although invisible to the human eye, it can be used to make things brighter!

Fluorescent, 'day-glo' paints contain chemicals which absorb the energy of invisible ultraviolet and give it off as visible light. It makes the paint look extra bright.

Some washing powders contain fluorescent dyes, called **brighteners**. They absorb ultraviolet and give off its energy as extra light, so your clothes look 'whiter than white'. Under ultraviolet disco lamps, some fabrics seem to glow!

In security-marking pens, the ink contains a fluorescent dye. The ink looks watery and can't normally be seen when dry. But a name or number written on your belongings shows up under a strong ultraviolet lamp.

Talking points

By using the index, or other sources of information, see if you can find out which type of electromagnetic radiation:

- is similar to gamma rays and has the same effects.
- is used for satellite communication and mobile phone networks.
- comes from warm or hot objects.
- is sent along optical fibres.

1

A

mirror

B

optical fibre

C

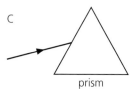

prism

a Copy and complete the diagrams above to show what will happen to the rays.

b Which of the above is an example of:
  i refraction;
  ii total internal reflection.

2 A teenager stands in front of a mirror and looks at his image.

Select three of these statments that correctly describe the image he sees in the mirror.

The image is as far behind the mirror as he is in front	A
The image is larger than the man	B
The image is the same size as the man	C
The image is smaller than the man	D
The image is upside down	E

3 The diagram below shows a ray of light entering a glass block.

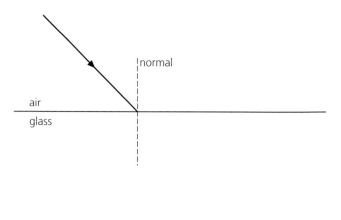

a Copy the diagram and draw in the path of the ray through the glass block.

b What happens to the ray as it enters and leaves the block?

c Explain why the ray behaves in this way.

d Draw a diagram to show what happens to a ray of light if it strikes the surface of the glass block at 90°.

4 The diagram below shows a man watching a fish swimming in a lake.

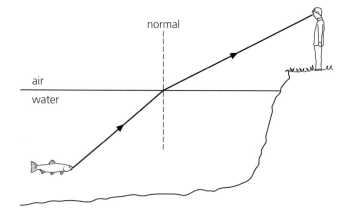

As the ray of light leaves the water it changes direction.

i Why does the ray change direction?

ii Copy the above diagram into your book. Mark on the diagram where the man sees the fish. Explain your answer.

5 The diagram below shows a simple prismatic periscope.

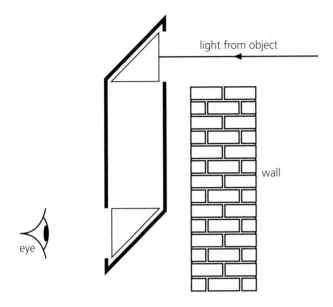

light from object

wall

eye

a Copy the diagram and then complete the path of the ray of light from the object to the eye.

b What happens to the ray of light inside each prism?

c Name one other device which makes use of this effect.

6 The diagram below shows a ray of light travelling through an optical fibre.

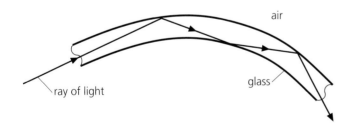

air

ray of light

glass

Explain what happens to the ray of light each time it strikes the boundary between the glass and the air.

7 White light is a mixture of many colours.

The diagram below shows how a prism can be used to split white light into these different colours.

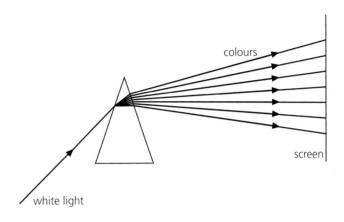

colours

screen

white light

a Copy this diagram and label the different colours as they are seen on the screen.

8 The diagram below shows sound waves being reflected from a hard flat surface.

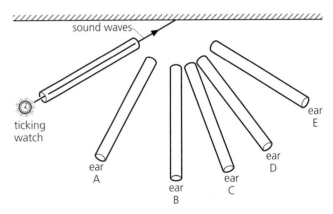

sound waves

ticking watch

ear A

ear B

ear C

ear D

ear E

In which position should the tube be placed to hear the ticking of the watch? Explain your choice.

9 A ship searching for fish emits sound waves which are reflected from the sea-bed. If the speed of sound in water is known and the time that elapses before the echo is heard is measured, it is possible to calculate how deep the water is at that point.

a What will the operator hear if a shoal of fish swims under the ship? How could the operator very roughly assess how deep the shoal is?

b Suggest one way in which the detector might be receiving a false signal (i.e. there are no fish below).

c If sound waves travel through water at 1500 m/s,

　i how deep is the sea-bed if the echo is heard after 1 s?

　ii how quickly is an echo heard if a shoal of fish swims 250 m below the ship?

10 A microphone is connected to an oscilloscope (CRO). When three different sounds, A, B and C, are made in front of the microphone, these are the waveforms seen on the screen:

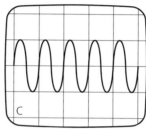

a Comparing sounds A and B, how would they sound different?

b Comparing sounds A and C, how would they sound different?

c Which sound has the highest amplitude?

d Which sound has the highest frequency?

e Sound A has a frequency of 220 Hz. If the speed of sound is 330 m/s, what is the wavelength of sound A?

f What is the frequency of sound C?

11 The diagram below shows the oscilloscope traces of two different sounds A and B. The oscilloscope setting is the same in both cases.

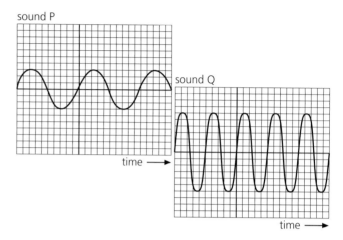

a A and B **sound** different.

Write down **two** differences in the way they sound.

Explain your answers as fully as you can.

12 A man standing on a beach 340 m from a tall cliff hears his echo after 2 s.

a What is an echo?

b Explain how echoes can be used to discover the depth of water under a boat.

c Using the information above calculate the speed of sound in air.

d What are ultrasonic waves?

e Give one use of ultrasonic waves.

13 a Sound X: frequency 10 000 Hz.

　Sound Y: frequency 30 000 Hz.

　Upper limit of human hearing: 20 000 Hz.

　i What is the upper limit of human hearing in kHz?

　ii Which of the above sounds is an example of ultrasound?

b Ultrasound can travel through some human tissues and can be reflected by different layers inside the body.

　i Describe one example of how ultrasound is used in hospitals.

　ii For producing medical images, why do doctors prefer to use ultrasound if they can, rather than X-rays?

　iii Describe one example of the industrial use of ultrasound.

14 This diagram shows the electromagnetic spectrum, but two types of radiation are missing from it.

a Which radiation should be in region A?

b Which radiation should be in region B?

radio waves	micro-waves	A	light	ultra-violet	B	gamma rays

c Which type of electromagnetic radiation:

   i has the shortest wavelength?

   ii has the lowest frequency?

   iii will diffract around hills?

   iv gives people a sun-tan?

   v can be used to cook food?

   vi can thermometers detect?

   vii can cause skin cancer?

   viii is used when taking a photograph with an ordinary camera?

d Which colour of visible light has:

   i the longest wavelength?

   ii the shortest wavelength?

15 a Draw a diagram of a wave. Label both its amplitude and its wave length.

b Your diagram represents a sound wave. What would you hear if

   i the wavelength got shorter?

   ii the amplitude got larger?

16 The diagram below shows a travelling sound wave.

a On a copy of the diagram show

   i the wavelength of the wave

   ii the amplitude of the wave

b Draw a second sound wave which is the same loudness as the first but has a higher frequency.

c Draw a third wave which has the same pitch as the first but represents a quieter sound.

d The sound wave in the above diagram was created in $\frac{1}{10}$ s. What is the frequency of this sound?

17 a Different types of electromagnetic radiation can be used for different jobs.

Choose words from this list to complete the table below.

**gamma rays   light   microwaves
radio waves   ultraviolet rays**

Type of radiation	One use of the radiation
	to send along optical fibres in an endoscope
	to give skin a tan
	to sterilize surgical instruments
	to send information to and from satellites

Write down one source of gamma radiation.

18 A solar heater is used to heat water.

a Which sort of energy heats the water?

b The solar heater is more efficient when a black container is used to hold the water rather than a white container. Explain why.

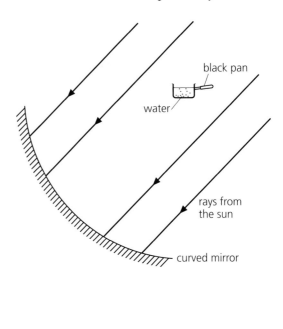

black pan

water

rays from the sun

curved mirror

Key words

The spread numbers in brackets tell you where to find more information.

amplitude For a wave displayed on the screen of an oscilloscope, this is the height of a 'peak' above the centre line. *(4.01, 4.11)*

analogue signals Signals which vary continuously in the same way as the source. *(4.08)*

critical angle If a ray strikes an internal face of a transparent block or liquid at an angle greater than this, all the light is reflected and none is refracted. *(4.06)*

diffraction The spreading or bending that occurs when waves travel through gaps or past obstacles. *(4.02, 4.08)*

digital signals Signals made up of a series of pulses, representing 0s and 1s. The 0s and 1s must be decoded to recreate the information being sent. *(4.08)*

echo A reflected sound, heard a short time after the original sound was sent out. *(4.10)*

electromagnetic waves A family of waves whose members are radio waves (including microwaves), infrared, light, ultraviolet, X-rays, and gamma rays. *(4.07)*

frequency The number of vibrations per second, or the number of waves per second. It is measured in hertz (Hz). If 100 waves are sent out per second, the frequency is 100 Hz. *(4.01, 4.11)*

hertz (Hz) Unit of frequency. If there are 100 vibrations per second, or 100 waves being sent out per second, the frequency is 100 Hz. *(4.01, 4.11)*

longitudinal waves Waves in which the oscillations (vibrations) are backwards and forwards. *(4.01)*

optical fibre Glass or plastic fibre, used in communications for carrying signals in the form of pulses of light or infrared. *(4.06, 4.08)*

period The time between one wavefront (or wave 'peak') passing and the next. *(4.01)*

pitch How high a note sounds to the ear. The higher the frequency of the sound waves, the higher the pitch. *(4.11)*.

plates Huge sections of the Earth's crust (and upper mantle) that slowly move on the material beneath them. *(4.14 – 4.15)*

refraction The bending that occurs when waves (such as light or sound waves) pass at an angle from one material into another. *(4.02, 4.05)*

seismic waves Vibrations that travel through the Earth and are caused by earthquakes. *(4.13)*

total internal reflection If light strikes an internal face of a transparent block or liquid at a large enough angle, all the light is reflected and none is refracted. This is called total internal reflection. *(4.06)*

transverse waves Waves in which the oscillations (vibrations) are from side to side (or up and down). *(4.01)*

ultrasound Sound waves with frequencies that are too high for the human ear to hear. *(4.12)*

wavelength The distance between wavefronts: in other words, the distance between one wave 'peak' and the next. *(4.01)*

Part of the Eagle Nebula, as seen by the *Hubble Space Telescope* from its orbit around the Earth. This vast pillar of gas and dust is billions of kilometres across. Within it, new stars are forming as matter is clumped together by the pull of gravity. The picture is also a view back in time. The nebula is so far away that its light takes 7000 years to reach the Earth.

Sun, Earth, Moon, and sky

Objectives

This spread should help you to

- Describe how the Moon and Earth orbit and turn
- Describe how the Moon and Earth are lit by the Sun

The Sun is a huge, hot, glowing ball of gas called a **star**. The Earth is a much smaller, cooler ball called a **planet**. The Sun is 150 million km away from us. Other stars only look like points of light because they are much further away.

Earth, orbiting and turning

As the Earth slowly turns on its axis, one half is in sunlight while the other half is in shadow.

The Earth moves round the Sun in a path called an **orbit**. One orbit takes just over 365 days, which is the length of our year.

As the Earth moves through space, it slowly turns about a line called its **axis**. This runs from the North Pole to the South Pole. It takes one day (24 hours) for the Earth to turn once. As it does so, places move from the sunlit half into the shadow half – in other words, from daytime into night. That is why the Sun appears to rise, move across the sky, and then set.

Questions

1 How long does it take the Earth to turn once on its axis?
2 How long does it take the Earth to orbit the Sun?

The Moon orbits the Earth, and the Earth orbits the Sun. All slowly turn on their axes the same way.

When you look at the Moon, you can only see the sunlit part.

The Moon

The Moon is in orbit around the Earth. The Moon takes about 28 days to complete each orbit. It also takes the same time to turn once on its axis, so it always keeps the same face toward us.

The Moon is smaller than the Earth (about a quarter of the diameter) and 380 000 km away. It has a rocky surface with lots of craters. Unlike the Sun, it is not hot and glowing. We can only see it because its surface reflects sunlight. And we don't see the part that is in shadow. That is why it sometimes looks like a crescent.

Looking at the sky

On a clear night, the sky is full of tiny points of light. Most of these are stars. Like the Sun, they appear to move across the sky as the Earth rotates. However, relative to each other, their positions hardly change by any amount that you could notice.

A few of the dots in the night sky *do* appear to change position. These are other planets in orbit around the Sun. (The word 'planet' comes from an old Greek word meaning 'wanderer'.)

During the daytime, you can't see stars or planets because their light is completely swamped by sunlight.

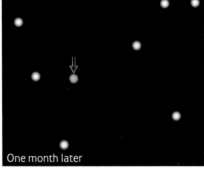

One month later

How the apparent position of a planet (Mars) can change relative to the stars.

Questions

3 Copy the diagram on the right. Shade in the part of the Earth that is in shadow. Then write down whether it is *daytime* or *night* at each of the following places:

    a Britain   **b** The North Pole   **c** The South Pole

4 As the Moon is not hot and glowing like the Sun, why are we able to see it?

5 If you watched it every night for several months, how could you tell whether a point of light in the night sky was a star or a planet?

not to scale

The Solar System (1)

Objectives

This spread should help you to

* explain what keeps the planets in orbit, and compare data about them

The Earth is one of many planets in orbit around the Sun. Some of these planets have smaller moons in orbit around them. Together, the Sun, planets, and other objects in orbit are known as the **Solar System**. This is far too big for the planets' sizes and distances from the Sun to be shown on the same scale diagram.

The further a planet is from the Sun, the slower it travels, and the more time its orbit takes.

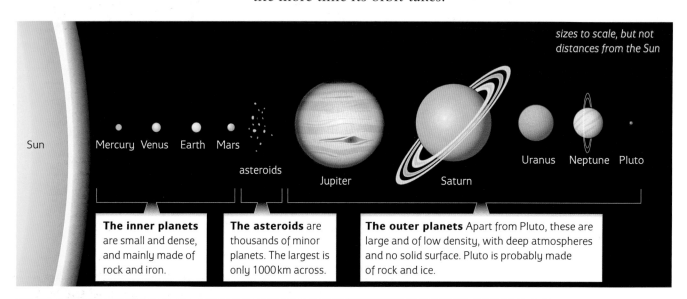

sizes to scale, but not distances from the Sun

The inner planets are small and dense, and mainly made of rock and iron.

The asteroids are thousands of minor planets. The largest is only 1000 km across.

The outer planets Apart from Pluto, these are large and of low density, with deep atmospheres and no solid surface. Pluto is probably made of rock and ice.

	Mercury	Venus	Earth	Mars	Jupiter	Saturn	Uranus	Neptune	Pluto
Average distance from Sun in million km	58	108	150	228	778	1427	2870	4490	5900
Time for one orbit in years	0.24	0.62	1	1.88	11.86	29.46	84.01	164.8	247
Diameter in km	4900	12 100	12 800	6800	143 000	120 000	51 000	49 000	2300
Mass compared with Earth (Earth = 1)	0.06	0.82	1.00	0.11	318	95.2	14.5	17.2	0.002
Average surface temp.	350°C	480°C	22°C	−23°C	−150°C	−180°C	−210°C	−220°C	−230°C
Number of moons	0	0	1	2	16	23	15	8	1

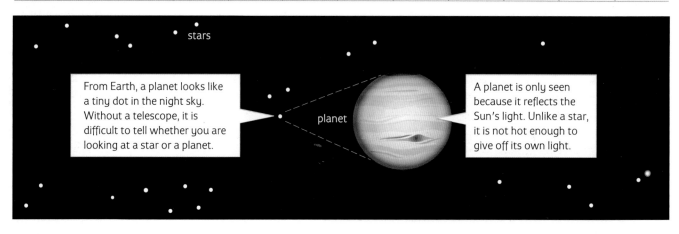

From Earth, a planet looks like a tiny dot in the night sky. Without a telescope, it is difficult to tell whether you are looking at a star or a planet.

A planet is only seen because it reflects the Sun's light. Unlike a star, it is not hot enough to give off its own light.

Orbits of the planets

Most of the inner and outer planets have near-circular orbits about the Sun. Most also orbit in the same plane (they are level with each other). However, Pluto's orbit is tilted.

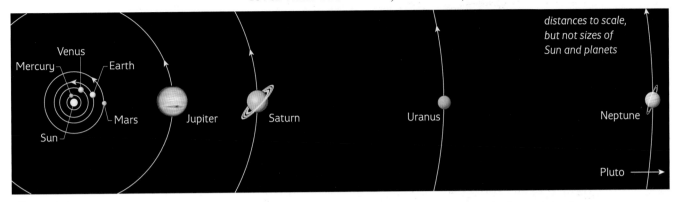

distances to scale, but not sizes of Sun and planets

Gravity in action

Gravity pulls us to the Earth. But scientists have found that there is a gravitational pull between *all* masses:

- Small masses have a weaker pull than large masses.
- Distant masses have a much weaker pull than close masses.

The pull between everyday things is far too weak to detect. It only becomes strong if one of the things has a huge mass, like a planet. The gravitational force between a planet and the Sun holds the planet in orbit around the Sun. Without it, the planet would drift off through space. The gravitational force between a moon and its planet holds the moon in orbit around the planet.

Questions

1 Which planets are smaller than the Earth?
2 Which planets have less mass than the Earth?
3 Which planet travels round the Sun at the highest speed?
4 **a** Which planets are colder than the Earth?
   b Why do you think that they are colder?
5 The diagram on the right shows the Sun and two planets.
   a What is the name of the force that holds the planets in their orbits?
   b Which of the two planets has the stronger force on it (assuming that both have about the same mass)?
   c Which of the two planets takes the longer time to go round the Sun?

d From Earth, Venus looks like a bright dot. Why does it look bright if it is not hot and glowing like a star?

e Carbon dioxide in Venus's atmosphere produces a severe greenhouse effect (global warming). What clue is there for this in the table on the opposite page?

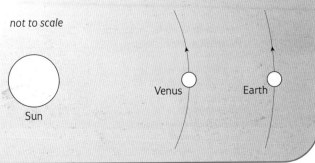

not to scale

Sun   Venus   Earth

The Solar System (2)

More about the planets

Mercury is the planet nearest the Sun. It has a cratered surface and no atmosphere.

Venus is the brightest object in the night sky (apart from the Moon). It is covered by thick clouds of sulphuric acid.

Earth is the only planet in the Solar System known to support life.

Mars is sometimes called the 'red planet' because of its surface colour. It has a thin atmosphere, a dusty surface, and polar caps.

The asteroids have diameters from a few kilometres up to 1000 km. Some have highly elliptical orbits (like 'stretched out' circles) which cross the paths of other planets.

Jupiter is more massive than all the other planets put together. It is mainly gas (hydrogen) and has no solid surface.

Saturn too is mainly gas. It is surrounded by a series of 'rings'.

Uranus is mainly gas and ice.

Neptune is similar to Uranus, but with a more violent atmosphere.

Pluto is small and icy. Its orbit is elliptical, and takes nearly 250 years to complete. Although called the 'outermost planet', it is actually inside Neptune's orbit at present.

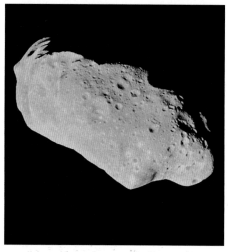

This asteroid, photographed by the Galileo spacecraft, is over 50 km long.

Saturn's rings are millions of pieces of ice and rock, each in its own orbit about the planet.

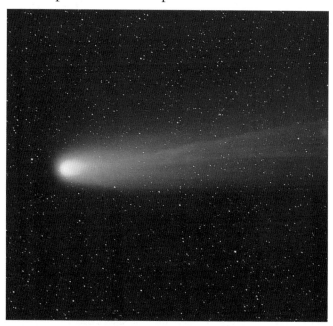

Halley's comet can be seen from Earth every 76 years. The last time was in 1986.

Comets, meteors, and meteorites

As well as the larger planets and asteroids, other objects orbiting the Sun include **comets** and millions of small bits of rock and ice.

Comets have highly elliptical orbits. A comet has least speed when furthest from the Sun. This is also when the Sun's gravitational pull on it is weakest. As it moves closer to the Sun, it speeds up.

In the 'head' of a comet, there is an icy lump, perhaps several kilometres across. Heated by the Sun, dust and gas stream off it into space, forming a huge 'tail' millions of kilometres long. This is visible because it reflects the sunlight.

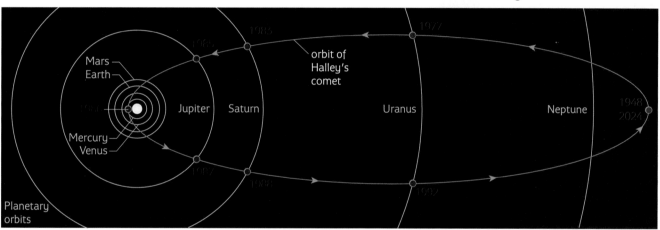

The orbit of Halley's comet. The red dots show where the comet was – or will be – between 1948 and 2024.

As the Earth moves through space, it runs into tiny grains of material which hit the atmosphere so fast that they burn up. Each one causes a streak of light called a **meteor**. Rarely, a larger chunk of material reaches the ground without completely burning up. The chunk is called a **meteorite**.

Questions

1 Which planet is most easily visible from Earth?

2 What are Saturn's rings?

3 If Pluto is now closer to the Sun than Neptune is, why is Pluto called the 'outermost planet'?

4 Why would it be difficult for astronauts to land on Jupiter?

5 What is the difference between a meteor and a meteorite?

6 The diagram on the right shows the orbit of a comet.

    a At what point (X, Y, or Z) is the Sun's gravitational pull on the comet strongest?

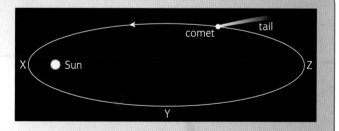

    b At what point does the comet have most speed?

    c At what point does the comet have least speed?

    d How is the tail of the comet formed?

    e Why is the tail of the comet visible?

Satellites in orbit

For a low polar orbit, a speed of 29 100 km/hour (18 100 m.p.h.) is required.

There are hundreds of satellites in orbit around the Earth. You can see some of the jobs they do on the opposite page.

To keep moving without power, satellites must be above the Earth's atmosphere, where there is no air resistance to slow them. A high orbit needs less speed than a low one. However, the launch rocket must leave the Earth faster in order to 'coast' further into space when its engines have burnt all their fuel and shut down.

Satellites that survey the Earth are often put into a low **polar orbit** – one that passes over the North and South Poles. As the Earth turns beneath them, they can scan the whole of its surface.

Communications satellites are normally put into a **geostationary orbit**. They orbit at the same rate as the Earth turns, so appear to stay in the same position in the sky. On the ground, the dish aerials sending and receiving the signals can point in a fixed direction.

Why a satellite stays up

In the 'thought experiment' below right, an astronaut is on a tall tower, above the atmosphere. She is so strong that she can throw a ball at the speed of a rocket!

Ball A is dropped. Gravity pulls it straight downwards.

Ball B is thrown horizontally. Gravity pulls it downwards, but it also moves sideways at a steady speed.

Ball C is also thrown horizontally, but so fast that the curve of its fall matches the curve of the Earth. The ball is in orbit. And with no air resistance to slow it, it will keep its speed and stay in orbit.

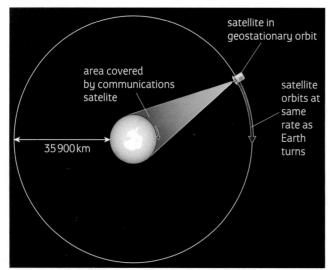

For a geostationary orbit, a satellite must be 35 900 km above the equator, with a speed of 11 100 km/hour.

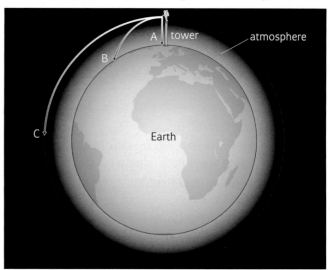

In this 'thought experiment', ball C is thrown so fast that it never reaches the ground. (See the section above.)

Communications satellites pass on telephone and TV signals from one place to another.

Some TVs get their pictures from a satellite like this.

Monitoring satellites study the weather and other conditions down on the Earth.

A picture taken from a weather satellite over Europe.

Research satellites Some of these carry telescopes for looking at stars and planets. Above the atmosphere, they get a much clearer view.

*This is the **Hubble Space Telescope**. It uses radio signals to send its pictures back to Earth.*

Navigation satellites send out radio signals which ships, aircraft, or people on the ground can use to find their position.

*This **GPS (global positioning system)** receiver uses time signals from satellites to calculate its position.*

Questions

1 A survey satellite is in a low polar orbit.
 a What is the advantage of this type of orbit?
 b Why must the satellite be above the atmosphere?
 c Give *three* other uses of satellites.

2 A satellite is launched from a rocket when the rocket is travelling horizontally. What will happen to the satellite if the rocket is:
 a too fast? **b** too slow?

3 TV satellites are in orbit and moving. Yet, down on the ground, the dish aerials that receive the signals point in a fixed direction. How is this possible?

4 Satellite A is put into one orbit around the Earth. Satellite B is put into a higher orbit.
 a Which satellite has the greater speed?
 b Which takes the longer time to orbit the Earth?

Sun, stars, and galaxies

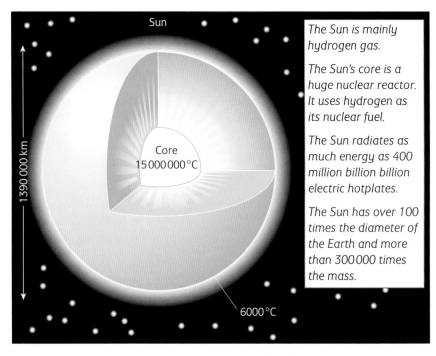

The Sun is mainly hydrogen gas.

The Sun's core is a huge nuclear reactor. It uses hydrogen as its nuclear fuel.

The Sun radiates as much energy as 400 million billion billion electric hotplates.

The Sun has over 100 times the diameter of the Earth and more than 300 000 times the mass.

Sun

1 390 000 km

Core 15 000 000 °C

6000 °C

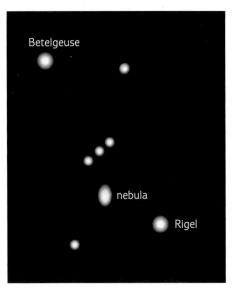

The constellation of Orion. Its stars aren't really in a group. Rigel is nearly twice as far away as Betelgeuse.

Betelgeuse

nebula

Rigel

The Sun is one star of billions. There are much bigger and brighter stars. However, from Earth, all the other stars look like tiny dots because they are so much further away.

Constellations

The brightest stars seem to form patterns in the sky. The different groups are called **constellations**. They have names like Orion, the Great Bear, and Pisces. But the stars in each constellation aren't really grouped together. For example, one star may be much further away than another, but look just as bright because it is bigger or hotter.

For practical reasons, astronomers still divide up the sky into constellations. It helps them find where different stars are.

Light years

Light is the fastest thing there is. But it can still take a long time to cover the vast distances in space:

Light travels at 300 000 kilometres per second. It takes...   *not to scale*

...8 minutes to reach us from the Sun

...6 hours to reach us from the furthest planet

...4 years to reach us from the nearest star

Astronomers have special units for measuring distances in space. For example: one **light year** is the distance travelled by light in one year. It is about 9 million million kilometres.

The nearest star to us (apart from the Sun) is Proxima Centauri. It is 4 light years away.

Galaxies

The Sun is a member of a huge star system called a **galaxy**. This contains over 100 billion stars, and is nearly 100 000 light years across. The galaxy is slowly rotating, and is held together by gravitational attraction.

Our galaxy is called the **Milky Way**. You can see the edge of its disc as a bright band of stars across the night sky. It is just one of many billions of galaxies in the known **Universe**.

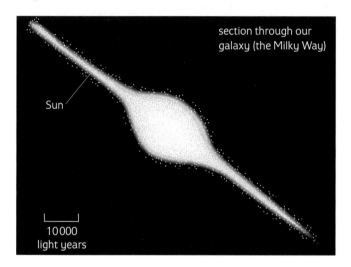

section through our galaxy (the Milky Way)

Sun

10 000 light years

Our own Sun is about halfway out from the centre of our galaxy.

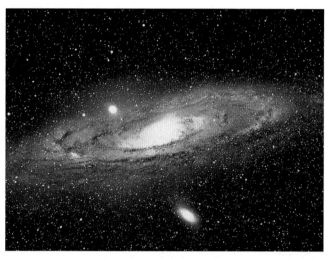

The Andromeda galaxy is 2 million light years away. Its light has taken 2 million years to reach us.

Questions

1 What substance is the Sun mostly made of?

2 What substance does the Sun use as its nuclear fuel?

3 Explain what is meant by these terms:
 a galaxy **b** Milky Way
 c constellation **d** light year

4 Stars in the same constellation appear to form a group.
 Are they really in a group? If not, explain why not.

5 Write down an approximate value for each of these:
 a the distance travelled by light in one second.

 b the number of stars in our galaxy.

 c the diameter of our galaxy, in light years.

 d how many times bigger the Sun's diameter is than the Earth's.

 e the time taken for light to travel from the Sun to the Earth.

 f the distance from Earth to the nearest star (apart from the Sun) in light years.

 g the number of kilometres in a light year.

 h the distance from Earth to the nearest star (apart from the Sun) in kilometres.

The life of a star

The Sun is a rather average, middle-aged star. This is the story of how a star such as the Sun is born, how it shines, and how it dies.

The birth of a star

Scientists think that the Sun and the rest of the Solar System formed about 4500 million years ago. It happened in a huge cloud of gas and dust called a **nebula**:

nebula of gas and dust
(about 4500 million years ago)

nuclear reactions start in Sun

not to scale

blob of matter begins to collect at centre

matter becomes more dense and hot

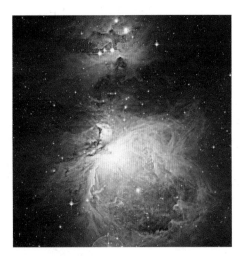

The Great Nebula in the constellation of Orion. Stars are born in clouds of gas and dust such as this.

In the nebula, gravity slowly pulled the gas and dust into blobs. In the centre, one blob grew bigger than all the rest. Around it, smaller blobs formed. Later, these would become planets and moons.

The Sun formed from the large blob in the centre. As gravity pulled in more and more material, the blob became hotter and hotter. Eventually, its core became so hot and compressed that nuclear reactions started, and the blob 'lit up' to become a star. Other stars formed – and are being formed – in the same way.

Energy from a star

The Sun is 75% hydrogen gas. It uses hydrogen as its fuel. Deep in its core, nuclear reactions release vast amounts of energy from hydrogen by changing it into helium.

Scientists think that the Sun has enough hydrogen left in its core to keep it shining for another 6000 million years.

The death of a star

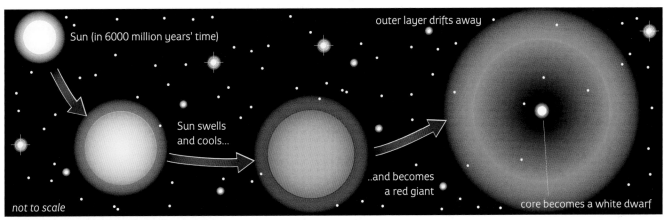

Sun (in 6000 million years' time)

outer layer drifts away

Sun swells and cools...

..and becomes a red giant

core becomes a white dwarf

not to scale

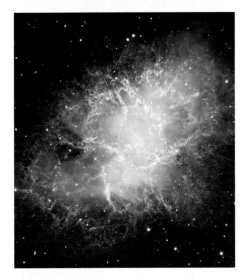

The Crab Nebula: the remains of a supernova.

In the Sun's core, the heating effect is so intense that it stops gravity pulling the material further inwards. However, in about 6000 million years' time, the core will have used up its hydrogen fuel, and will collapse. At the same time, the Sun's outer layer will expand and cool to a red glow. The Sun will have changed into a type of star called a **red giant**.

Eventually, the Sun's outer layer will drift into space, leaving a hot, dense core called a **white dwarf**. This tiny star will use helium as its fuel. When the helium runs out, the star will fade for ever.

Supernovae and black holes

If a star is much more massive than the Sun, it dies a different death. It blows up in a gigantic nuclear explosion called a **supernova**, leaving a very dense core called a **neutron star**.

When the most massive stars of all explode, the core cannot resist the pull of gravity and goes on collapsing. The result is a **black hole**. Nothing can escape from a black hole, not even light. There may be a black hole at the centre of every galaxy.

Questions

1 Like other stars, the Sun formed in a *nebula*.

   a What is a nebula?

   b What made matter in the nebula collect together in blobs?

   c About how long ago was the Sun formed?

   d What else formed in the nebula at the same time as the Sun?

2 The Sun gets its energy from nuclear reactions.

   a Where in the Sun do these reactions take place?

   b What fuel is the Sun using for these reactions?

   c About how long will it be before this fuel runs out?

3 One day, the Sun will become a *red giant*.

   a What is a red giant?

   b What will eventually happen to the Sun, after it has been a red giant?

4 **a** What is a *supernova*?

   b After a supernova has occurred, what is left at its centre?

The expanding Universe

Stars are made from matter from the big bang, and we are made from matter from stars.

There are billions of galaxies in the Universe. The most distant ones are so far away that their light has taken more than 10 billion years to reach us. The light started its journey almost right back at the beginning of time itself.

In the 1920s, Edwin Hubble analysed the light coming from distant galaxies. From changes to the light, he reached the conclusion that the galaxies must be rushing apart at high speed. We seem to be living in an expanding Universe.

The big-bang theory

According to this theory, the Universe began more than 10 billion years ago when a single, incredibly dense, hot 'superatom' expanded in a burst of energy called the **big bang**. This was the beginning of time. Everything in the Universe came from it.

Here are two pieces of evidence to support this idea:

• As the galaxies appear to be rushing apart, they may once have come from the same tiny volume of space.
• Radio telescopes like the one in the photograph below have picked up faint background radiation from every direction in space. This may be an 'echo' of the big bang.

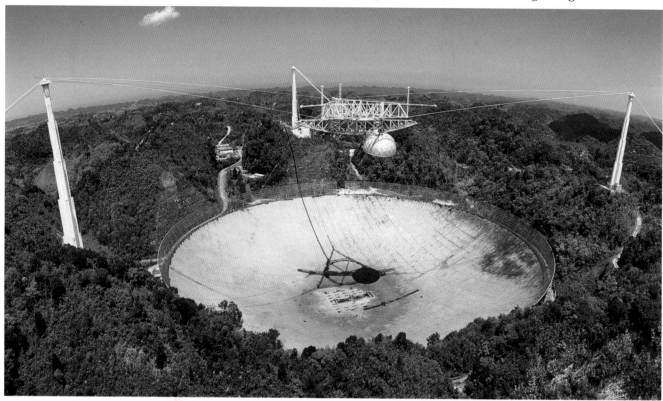

Stars give out radio waves, as well as light and other forms of radiation. Radio telescopes like this can detect the faintest radio signals coming from the most distant galaxies, and pinpoint where they are coming from.

The big bang wasn't an explosion into empty space that was already there. The big bang *created* space, which then started to expand. Most people find this very difficult to imagine, which is why the balloon model below may help. Here, space is represented by the stretching surface of an inflating balloon.

big bang

galaxies move apart as Universe expands

A balloon model of an expanding Universe.

Imagine that you are on one of the galaxies as the balloon inflates. It doesn't matter which galaxy you are on. All the other galaxies appear to be moving away from you.

The fate of the Universe

What will happen to the Universe in the future? Scientists aren't sure. Until recently, they thought that gravitational attraction might be slowing down the expansion. Perhaps the galaxies would stop rushing apart and be pulled back together again. Perhaps time would end in a big crunch! But recently, some scientists have been getting some very puzzling results. These suggest that the expansion may actually be speeding up, but no one knows why.

Questions

1 What observation first gave scientists the idea that the Universe might be expanding?

2 According to the big-bang theory, the Universe began when a single, incredibly dense, hot 'superatom' expanded in a burst of energy. Give *two* pieces of evidence that support this idea.

3 According to the big-bang theory, approximately how old is the Universe?

4 Some galaxies are far too distant and faint to be seen with an ordinary telescope, especially where clouds of gas and dust in space stop the light getting through. How can scientists get information about these galaxies?

5 Until recently, scientists thought that the expansion of the Universe might be slowing down.

   a What force did they think was slowing it down?

   b What new results are proving difficult to explain?

Looking for life

Scientists would love to find evidence of intelligent life out in space. They would be happy to find *any* form of life, even simple bacteria. But so far, their search is proving difficult.

A home for life

The Earth is a special place. It has the rare conditions that make life possible, including liquid water, and a distance from the Sun which makes the temperature just right. It even has a big bodyguard, Jupiter, whose gravitational pull stops many comets and asteroids smashing into it.

But is Earth the only home for life? Within the Solar System, two other candidates are Mars and Europa – a moon of Jupiter. Mars seems to be a dead planet now, but water once flowed there, and simple life may have lived there. Europa has a warm interior and may have liquid water beneath its icy surface.

Living things change the land, sea, and air. For example, if life had not evolved on Earth, there would be much less oxygen in our atmosphere and no fossils in the rocks. So conditions on Mars and Europa may give clues about the existence of life there now or in the past.

Does life only exist on Earth?

... Or could it exist beneath the icy surface of Europa?

... Or on Mars? This wheeled robot found no evidence of life when it landed there. But future explorations might reveal something.

Europa

SETI

Spacecraft can be sent to places in our Solar System, but a visit to even the nearest star would take thousands of years. If we want to detect life far out in space, we have to hope that the life is intelligent and sending out radio signals. The search for these signals is called the **SETI** project (the **Search for Extra-Terrestrial Intelligence**). It has been going on for over 40 years.

Radio telescopes like the one here are used to detect natural radio waves coming from stars. SETI scientists also use them to search for signals that might have been made by intelligent life.

If signals are ever found, communicating with their senders will be almost impossible. Radio waves take about 4 years to reach us from the nearest star, and 2 million years from our neighbouring galaxy, Andromeda. If we send signals now, it will be 2 million years before any Andromedans receive them.

Little green men

In the late 1960s, the physicist Jocelyn Bell was analysing data from a radio telescope, when she noticed strange signals coming from a distant star. They were pulses so regular and rapid that, for a while, no one thought that they could be natural. Maybe the signals had been sent by distant aliens, or 'little green men' as they became known.

The **LGM** (**little green men**) theory was soon abandoned. What Jocelyn Bell had discovered was a new type of star called a **pulsar** – a rapidly spinning neutron star. It sends out radio beams whose pulses are rather like the flashes seen when a lighthouse beam sweeps round and round.

Maybe the next time strange pulses are found, they really will be coming from little green men.

Talking points

Can you explain why, in the immediate future, astronauts are unlikely to visit planets around other stars?

Can you explain what the SETI project is?

Can you explain why, if we pick up radio signals from distant aliens, we won't be able to exchange messages with them?

1 Copy and complete the sentences below choosing words from this list:

Galaxy planet satellite constellation star

a The Sun is a _____.

b The Moon is a natural _____.

c A small group of stars, as seen from the Earth, is called a _____.

d The Milky Way is the name of our _____.

2

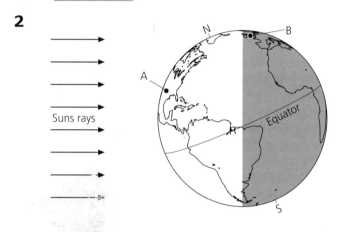

a Explain why it is daytime at A.

b Explain why it is night-time at B.

c How long does it take for the Earth to complete one rotation?

d The Earth has one natural satellite. What is it called?

e What forces keep the Earth in orbit around the Sun?

f Mercury and Venus are two planets that are closer to the Sun than the Earth. Are the forces they experience larger or smaller than those experienced by the Earth? Explain your answer.

3 a Name one luminous object in the night sky.

b Name one non-luminous object in the night sky.

c The diagrams show the constellation Taurus on two nights a month apart.

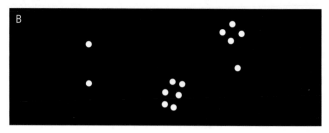

i What evidence is there that one of the objects is a planet? Make a sketch to show which object it is.

ii Why will the planet not always appear to be among the stars of Taurus?

d i What is a satellite?

ii Name one artificial satellite.

4 The diagram below shows two identical satellites, A and B, in orbit around the Earth.

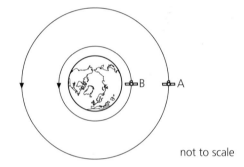

not to scale

a Which satellite is pulled most strongly by the Earth's gravitational field?

b Which satellite has the highest speed?

c Which satellite will take longest to complete one orbit of the Earth?

d Satellite A is in a geostationary orbit. What does this mean?

e Why are communications satellites normally put into geostationary orbits?

5 The diagram shows the path of a satellite placed in a low polar orbit round the Earth.

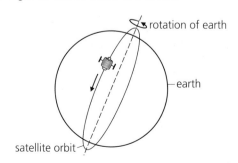

It takes the above satellite 2 hours to orbit the Earth.

a How many orbits will the satellite complete in one full day?

b Explain why a low polar orbit is useful for weather satellites.

c Describe one other use for a satellite in this kind of orbit.

d Why would this kind of orbit be no use for a communications satellite?

e What is a geostationary orbit?

6 Here is some data about the planets:

Planet	Diameter of planet in km	Average distance from Sun in million km	Time for one orbit in years	Average surface temperature in °C
Mercury	4900	58	0.2	350
Venus	12000	108	0.6	480
Earth	12800	150	1.0	22
Mars	6800	228	1.9	–23
Jupiter	143000	778	11.9	–150
Saturn	120000	1427	29.5	–180
Uranus	52000	2870	84.0	–210
Neptune	49000	4497	164.8	–220
Pluto	3000	5900	247.8	–230

Use the above table to answer the following questions.

a Which is the largest planet?

b Which is the smallest planet?

c Which planet is closest to the Sun?

d Which planet takes almost twelve Earth years to orbit the Sun?

e How long is a year on the planet Mercury? Explain your answer.

f How would you expect a planet's surface temperature to depend on its distance from the Sun? Does the data in the above table support this? Explain your answer.

7 The graph below shows the orbit times and average distance from the Sun for several planets.

a Which planet experiences the largest gravitational forces from the Sun?

b Which planet experiences the smallest gravitational forces from the Sun?

c Explain why Jupiter takes longer to orbit the Sun than Venus.

d Between which planets is the asteroid belt?

e Estimate the orbit time for an asteroid in the middle of the belt.

f What is the shape of the orbits of the planets and the asteroids?

8

meteorite	galaxy	supernova
big bang	constellation	black hole
moon	comet	Solar System

Which of the above is the best match for each of the following descriptions?

a A rocky object orbiting a planet.

b The Sun, its planets, and other objects in orbit.

c A small rocky object which collides with a planet, and may be a fragment from an asteroid.

d A clump of ice, gas and dust, usually in a highly elliptical orbit around the Sun.

e A huge group of many millions of stars.

f A gigantic explosion that occurs when a very massive star has used up its nuclear fuel.

The spread numbers in brackets tell you where to find more information.

asteroids Sometimes called minor planets, these lumps of rock mostly have orbits between those of Mars and Jupiter. *(5.02 – 5.03)*

big-bang theory The theory that the Universe was created when a single, incredibly dense, hot 'superatom' expanded, more than 10 billion years ago. *(5.07)*

black hole What is left when a very massive star collapses at the end of its life. A black hole's gravity is so strong that nothing can escape, not even light. *(5.06)*

comet An icy lump of material that moves around the Sun in a highly elliptical orbit. Its 'tail' is a thin stream of gas and dust that reflects sunlight. *(5.03)*

constellation Stars that appear to form a group or pattern when viewed from Earth. Usually, the stars are at different distances and not related at all. *(5.05)*

galaxy A huge system of billions of stars. *(5.05, 5.07)*

geostationary orbit An orbit specially chosen so that a satellite appears stationary in the sky. This is because it orbits at the same rate as the Earth turns. *(5.04)*

light year The distance travelled by light in one year. It is nearly 10 000 000 000 000 kilometres. *(5.05)*

meteorite A lump of rock from space that strikes the Earth (or other planet or moon). *(5.03)*

moon large, rocky object that orbits a planet. *(5.01-5.02)*

nebula A huge cloud of gas and dust in space. In it, new stars are formed. *(5.06)*

neutron star The very dense core of a supernova. *(5.06)*

orbit Circular or elliptical path followed by an object as it moves around a planet, moon, or Sun. *(5.01 – 5.04)*

planet large object (such as the Earth) that orbits a star (such as the Sun). *(5.01 – 5.02)*

red giant A star near the end of its life, which has expanded and is glowing red. *(5.06)*

satellite Any object that orbits the Earth (or other planet). Most satellites are put into orbit by rockets. However, the Moon is a natural satellite of the Earth. *(5.04)*

star A huge, hot, glowing ball of gas, such as the Sun. It is powered by nuclear reactions. *(5.01, 5.05 – 5.06)*

Sun This is a star. *(5.01, 5.05 – 5.06)*

supernova A gigantic explosion that occurs when a massive star is at the end of its life. *(5.06)*

Universe All the galaxies: everything that exists. *(5.05, 5.07)*

white dwarf The hot, dense core left when a red giant star has lost its outer layer. *(5.06)*

Energy

The Niagara falls, on the USA–Canada border. The photograph shows the highest section of the falls, where the water tumbles over 30 metres to the river below. Nearly three million litres of water flow over the falls every second. Most of the energy is wasted, but some is harnessed by a hydroelectric power station which generates electricity for the surrounding area.

Work and energy

Work

This tennis player is doing work. So she is using energy.

You do work when you climb the stairs, lift a bag, or hit a tennis ball. To scientists, work is done whenever a force makes something move. The greater the force, and the further it moves, the more work is done.

Work is measured in **joules** (J). 1 joule of work is done when a force of 1 newton (N) makes something move a distance of 1 metre (m).

There is an equation for calculating work:

work done = force × distance moved
(in the direction of the force)
in J   in N   in m

For example, the shopper below uses a 10 N force to push a trolley a distance of 3 m. So:

work done = force × distance moved = 10 × 3 = 30 J

Questions

1 What unit is used for measuring work?

2 Amna uses a force of 20 N to push a lawnmower 4 m. How much work does she do?

3 How much work would Amna do if she pushed the lawnmower twice as far?

Energy

Things have energy if they can do work. A falling stone has energy. So do a stretched spring and a tankful of petrol. Each can be used to make something move.

Energy can exist in different forms:

Kinetic energy

This is the energy things have because they are moving.

Radiated energy

Light and sound are both forms of energy which radiate (spread) from their source.

Thermal energy (heat)*

This is the energy which comes from hot things when they cool down.

Potential energy

This is stored energy. Here are some examples:

A stretched spring has elastic potential energy.

A rock on the top of a cliff has gravitational potential energy. The energy is released when gravity makes it fall.

Foods, fuels, and batteries have chemical energy. Their energy is released by chemical reactions (for example, by burning a fuel).

Wires carry electrical energy to drills, lamps, and other appliances.

Radioactive materials store nuclear energy.

Everything is made of tiny particles (atoms or molecules). These are constantly on the move, so they have energy. The higher the temperature, the faster they move, and the more energy they have.

Like work, energy is measured in joules (**J**). For each joule of work done, one joule of energy must be used.

Larger units of energy (and work) are the **kilojoule** and the **megajoule**:

1 kilojoule (kJ) = 1000 J   1 megajoule (MJ) = 1 000 000 J

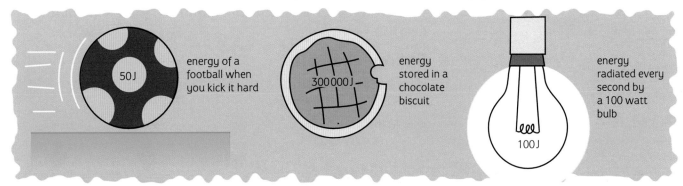

energy of a football when you kick it hard — 50 J

energy stored in a chocolate biscuit — 300 000 J

energy radiated every second by a 100 watt bulb — 100 J

Questions

4 What unit is used for measuring energy?

5 Give *two* examples of things whose stored energy can be released by chemical reactions.

6 Look at the diagram above, showing the football, chocolate biscuit, and bulb.

a What form of energy does the moving football have?

b How much energy does the chocolate biscuit store, in kilojoules (kJ)?

c How much energy does the light bulb radiate in one minute?

Energy changes

Energy doesn't vanish when you use it. It just goes somewhere else! The diagram below is an example of how energy can change from one form to another. It is sometimes called an **energy chain**:

In every energy chain, the total amount of energy stays the same. Scientists express this idea in the **law of conservation of energy**:

Energy can change into different forms, but it cannot be made or destroyed.

| chemical energy | → | kinetic energy | → | gravitational potential energy | → | kinetic energy | → | thermal energy (heat) |

Above, when the weights hit the ground, they make the atoms and molecules in the ground – and themselves – move a little faster. So their kinetic energy is changed into thermal energy (heat). In any chain, energy is always wasted as heat. For example, you give off heat when you exercise, which is why you sweat! However, the *total* amount of energy (including heat) stays the same.

Energy changers

Here are some examples of energy changers in action:

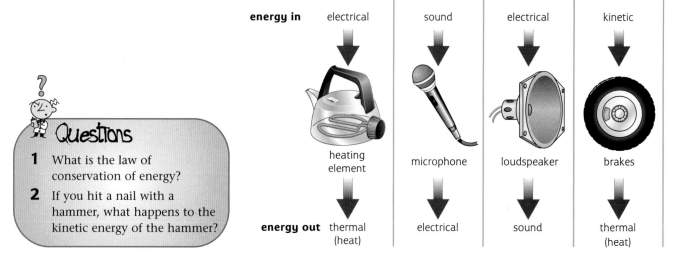

energy in	electrical	sound	electrical	kinetic
	↓	↓	↓	↓
	heating element	microphone	loudspeaker	brakes
	↓	↓	↓	↓
energy out	thermal (heat)	electrical	sound	thermal (heat)

Questions

1 What is the law of conservation of energy?

2 If you hit a nail with a hammer, what happens to the kinetic energy of the hammer?

Lifting and dropping

For every joule (J) of work you do on something, it gains 1 J of energy.

Below, a stone of mass 2 kilograms (kg) is lifted to a height of 5 metres (m) and then dropped. Knowing this, you can calculate the following:

1 The work done in lifting the stone.
2 The gravitational potential energy of the stone after lifting.
3 The kinetic energy of the stone just before it hits the ground.

Follow the calculations through in order. But first, read the panel on the left, telling you about the link between mass and weight.

1 Work done in lifting the stone
This is calculated using the equation:

work done = force × distance moved
   in J   in N   in m

In this case, the force used must match the weight in order to lift it. For a 2 kg mass, the weight is 20 N.
So:

work done = weight × height lifted
         =   20   ×   5
         =   100 J

So: the work done is 100 J

2 kg

5 m

2 Gravitational potential energy of the stone

This is equal to the work done in lifting the stone. So:

The gravitational potential energy is 100 J

3 Kinetic energy of the stone

As the stone falls, its gravitational potential energy is changed into kinetic energy. If no energy is wasted because of air resistance, *all* the gravitational potential energy becomes kinetic energy. So:

The kinetic energy is 100 J

Questions

3 *pole vaulter*   *sprinter*   *electric toaster*   *battery*

Which of the above:

a changes electrical energy into thermal energy (heat)?

b changes kinetic energy into gravitational potential energy?

c changes chemical energy into kinetic energy?

4 Describe the energy changes that take place when you apply the brakes on a moving cycle.

5 Scientists say that energy can 'never be destroyed'. Explain what they mean.

6 What is the weight (in N) of each kg of mass, on Earth?

7 A rock of mass 4 kg is lifted to a height of 6 m above the ground and then dropped.

a What is the weight of the rock (in N)?

b How much work is done in lifting the rock to a height of 6 m?

c What is the gravitational potential energy of the rock at a height of 6 m?

d What is the kinetic energy of the rock just before it hits the ground?

e When the rock hits the ground, what happens to its energy?

Energy and work

Objectives

This spread should help you to

- calculate gravitational potential energy and kinetic energy
- explain why 'speed kills'

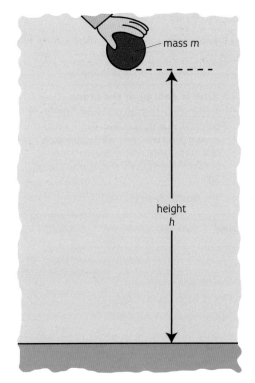

mass *m*

height
h

These skiers have gravitational potential energy (GPE for short). They also have kinetic energy (KE). Both GPE and KE can be calculated.

Calculating GPE

If something is above the ground, as on the left, its GPE in joules (J) can be calculated like this:

$$GPE = mgh$$

m is the mass of the object in kg
g is the Earth's gravitational field strength (10 N/kg)
h is the height above the ground, in metres (m)

For example, if a stone of mass 2 kg is 5 m above the ground:

$$GPE = mgh = 2 \times 10 \times 5 = 100J$$

The above equation is really another way of saying that the GPE is equal to the work done in lifting the stone in the first place. For example, on Earth the 2 kg stone has a weight of 20 N. So a force of 20 N is needed to lift it. And if it is lifted a height of 5 m:

$$\text{work done} = \text{force} \times \text{distance moved} = 20 \times 5 = 100J$$

Calculating KE

The kinetic energy of a moving object can be calculated like this:

$$KE = \tfrac{1}{2}mv^2$$

m is the mass of the object in kg
v is the speed of the object in metres per second (m/s)

There are two examples at the top of the next page.

$KE = \frac{1}{2}mv^2$
$= \frac{1}{2} \times 2 \times 3^2$
$= 9\,J$

$KE = \frac{1}{2}mv^2$
$= \frac{1}{2} \times 2 \times 6^2$
$= 36\,J$

Speed dangers

The above calculations show that if the speed of something *doubles*, it has *four times* as much kinetic energy. This is one of the reasons why road safety experts say that 'speed kills'. Think of the effect on a car which doubles its speed. If the car brakes normally, it will need about four times the distance to stop. If, instead, it hits a crash barrier, or another car, or a pedestrian, it will cause much more damage or injury because of all the extra energy it has to lose.

Work done and energy transformed

Scientifically speaking, when energy changes from one form to another, energy is **transformed** (some books say **transferred** instead).

Whenever energy is transformed, work is done. For example, on the left, a falling brick loses 100J of GPE. Assuming no air resistance, this is changed into 100J of KE. So 100J of work is done in accelerating the brick. When the brick hits the ground, 100J of KE is changed into heat (thermal energy). Again 100J of work is done as the brick flattens the ground beneath it. In each case:

work done = energy transformed

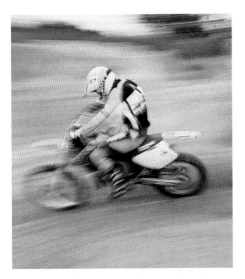

Extra speed means much more kinetic energy, which can be dangerous.

100J GPE

100J KE

100J heat

| 100J energy in one form | | 100J work done | | 100J energy in another form |

Questions

1 A 4kg brick is held 3m above the ground. If $g = 10\,N/kg$:

   a what is the GPE of the brick?

   b what will its GPE be if its height above the ground is doubled?

2 **a** In question **1**, how much work would you have to do to lift the brick 3m?

   b How much energy is transformed during this lift?

3 If a 4kg brick is falling at a speed of 2m/s:

   a what is the KE of the brick?

   b what will its KE be if it falls at twice the speed?

4 A driver thinks that if he doubles his speed, and then has to brake, the distance needed to stop his car will only be about twice what it was before. Is he correct? If not, why not?

Conduction and convection

Objectives

This spread should help you to

- describe how energy can travel by thermal conduction and convection
- describe how insulating materials are used

Good conductors

metals	e.g.	copper
		aluminium
		iron
silicon		
graphite		

Poor conductors (insulators)

glass

water

plastics

rubber

wood

materials containing trapped air	wool
	glass wool (fibreglass)
	plastic foam
	expanded polystyrene

The materials above are arranged in order of conducting ability, starting with the best.

Thermal conduction

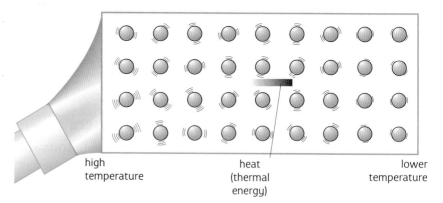

high temperature   heat (thermal energy)   lower temperature

All materials are made up of tiny, moving particles (atoms or molecules). The higher the temperature, the faster they move. If one end of a metal bar is heated, as above, heat (**thermal energy**) is transferred from the hot end to the cold as the faster particles pass on their extra movement to those all along the bar. The energy is travelling by **thermal conduction** (or **conduction**, for short).

Metals are the best **conductors** of heat. Non-metal solids tend to be poor conductors, and so do most liquids. Gases are the worst of all. Bad conductors are called **insulators**. Many materials are insulators because they contain pockets of trapped air.

Convection

Liquids and gases are poor conductors, but if they are free to circulate, they can carry heat with them. There is an example below. Here, the air in a room is being warmed by a heater. The warm air rises as cooler, denser air sinks and displaces it (pushes it out of the way). The result is a circulating stream, called a **convection** current. This carries heat to other parts of the room.

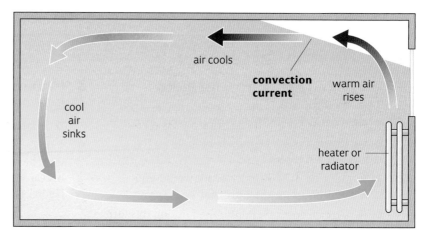

air cools

convection current

warm air rises

cool air sinks

heater or radiator

Convection can also happen in liquids. For example, hot water rises when it is displaced by cooler, denser water sinking around it. That is why, in a hot water storage tank like the one in the diagram below, the hottest water collects at the top.

Using insulating materials

In a house, good insulation means lower fuel bills. Below, you can see some of the ways in which insulating materials are used to reduce heat losses:

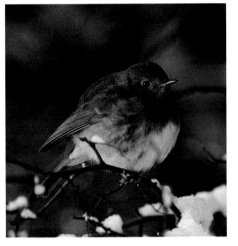

Feathers are a good thermal insulator, especially when fluffed up to trap more air.

1 Plastic foam lagging round the hot water storage tank.
2 Glass or mineral wool insulation in the loft.
3 Wall cavity filled with plastic foam, beads, or mineral wool.
4 Double-glazed windows: two sheets of glass with air between.

Some insulating materials have a shiny, metallic coating to reduce heat losses by thermal radiation (explained in the next spread).

Questions

1 Which materials are the best conductors?
2 Why are wool and feathers good insulators?
3 Explain each of the following:
  a A saucepan might have a copper bottom but a plastic handle.
  b Someone feels cold in a string vest, but warm if they wear a tight shirt over it.
  c It is safer picking up hot dishes with a dry cloth than a wet one.

4 Explain each of the following:
  a A radiator quickly warms all the air in a room, even though air is a poor thermal conductor.
  b Anyone standing near a bonfire feels a draught.
  c If a hot water storage tank has an immersion heater (electric heating element), this is fitted near the bottom of the tank rather than near the top.
5 Give *three* ways in which insulating materials are used to reduce heat losses from a house.

Objectives

This spread should help you to

- explain what surfaces are best at emitting and absorbing thermal radiation
- describe how a solar panel and a vacuum flask work

On Earth, we are warmed by the Sun. Its energy travels to us as tiny **electromagnetic waves**. These include invisible **infrared** waves as well as light, and they can travel through empty space. They heat up things that absorb them, so are often called **thermal radiation**.

All things emit (send out) some thermal radiation. The hotter they are, the more energy they radiate per second.

Emitters and absorbers

Some surfaces are better at emitting thermal radiation than others. The chart on the next page shows how surfaces compare. Good emitters of radiation are also good absorbers. White or silvery surfaces are poor absorbers because they reflect most of the radiation away. That is why, in hot, sunny countries, houses are often painted white to keep them cool inside.

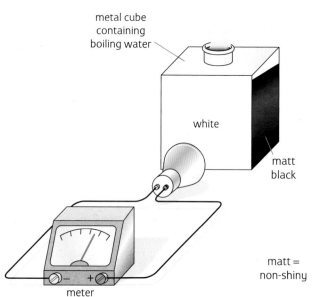

Comparing emitters *The metal cube is filled with boiling water. This heats the surfaces to the same temperature. The thermal radiation detector is placed in turn at the same distance from each surface and the meter readings compared.*

Comparing absorbers *The metal plates are placed at the same distance from a radiant heater. To find out which surface absorbs thermal radiation quickest, the rises in temperature are compared.*

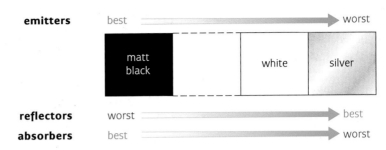

emitters	best	→			worst

matt black		white	silver

reflectors	worst	→	best
absorbers	best	→	worst

This chart shows how some surfaces compare as emitters, reflectors, and absorbers of thermal radiation.

The solar panel

The **solar panel** above uses the Sun's thermal radiation to warm up water for the house. The blackened layer absorbs the radiant energy and warms the water flowing through the pipes.

The vacuum flask

A vacuum flask can keep drinks hot (or cold) for hours. It has these features for reducing how quickly energy flows out (or in):

1 A stopper to reduce convection (hot air rising).
2 A double-walled container with a gap between the walls. Air has been removed from the gap to reduce conduction.
3 Walls with silvery surfaces to reduce thermal radiation.

❶ stopper

❷ gap with air removed

glass or steel walls

❸ silvery surfaces

A vacuum flask.

Questions

1 *white   silvery   matt black*
Which of the above surfaces is the best at:
  a absorbing thermal radiation?
  b emitting thermal radiation?
  c reflecting thermal radiation?
2 Why does the solar panel above have:
  a a blackened layer at the back?
  b a network of water pipes?

3 What feature does a vacuum flask have to stop it losing (or gaining) heat by thermal radiation?
4 Explain why:
  a In hot countries, houses are often painted white.
  b On a hot summer's day, if cars are left in a car park, the inside of a white car is cooler than a black one.
  c Aluminium foil helps keep food dishes warm when they're out on the table.

Efficiency and power

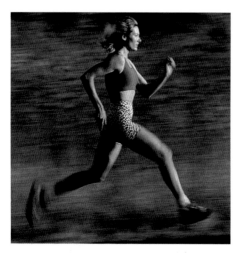

Human 'engines' (muscles) have an efficiency of about 15%.

Engines and motors do work by making things move. To do this, engines use the energy in their fuel. Electric motors use energy from a battery or generator. Even your body is a type of engine. It uses the energy in your food.

Efficiency

An engine does useful work with some of the energy put into it, but the rest is wasted as heat. The **efficiency** of an engine can be calculated as follows (the two versions mean the same thing):

$$\text{efficiency} = \frac{\text{useful work done}}{\text{energy input}} \quad \text{or efficiency} = \frac{\text{useful energy output}}{\text{energy input}}$$

For example, if a petrol engine does 25J of useful work for every 100J of energy put into it, then its efficiency is 0.25, or 25%. In other words, its useful energy output is $\frac{1}{4}$ of its total energy input.

Here are some typical efficiencies:

Energy input			Useful work done	Efficiency
100J	petrol engine		25J	25%
100J	diesel engine		35J	35%
100J	electric motor		80J	80%

Although electric motors have a high efficiency, the efficiency of the power stations that generate the electricity for them is only about 35%.

Power

A small engine can do just as much work as a big engine, but it takes longer to do it. The big engine can do work at a faster rate. The rate at which work is done is called the **power**.

Power is measured in **watts** (W). A power of 1watt means that work is being done at the rate of 1J per second. Put another way, energy is being used at the rate of 1J per second.

Power is calculated like this:

$$\text{power} = \frac{\text{work done}}{\text{time taken}} \quad \text{or} \quad \text{power} = \frac{\text{energy used}}{\text{time taken}}$$

Questions

1 A motor has an *efficiency* of 50%. Explain in words what this means.

2 One engine has twice the *power* of another. Explain in words what this means.

For example, if an engine does 1000J of useful work in 2 seconds, its power output is 500 watts (500J per second).

Powers are sometimes given in **kilowatts** (kW). 1 kW = 1000 W.

Typical power outputs

250W — washing machine motor
400W — human engine
45 000W (45 kW) — small car engine
85 000W (85 kW) — Land Rover engine

Here is another way of calculating an engine's efficiency:

$$\text{efficiency} = \frac{\text{useful power output}}{\text{power input}}$$

The model crane on the left can lift a mass of 4 kg through a height of 3 metres in 10 seconds. This is how you would calculate its useful power output:

mass: 4kg
time taken: 10s
height lifted: 3m

○ Calculate the force being moved. (This is the weight being lifted. On Earth, it is 10N for each kg of mass.)

force (weight) = 4 × 10 = 40 N

○ Use work = force × distance to calculate the useful work done.

useful work done = 4 × 3 = 120 J

○ Use power = $\frac{\text{work done}}{\text{time taken}}$ to calculate the useful power output.

useful power output = $\frac{120}{10}$ = 12 W

Questions

3 With each 5000J of energy supplied to it by its fuel, an engine does 2000J of useful work.

  a What is its efficiency?

  b What happens to the rest of the energy supplied?

4 If an engine does 800J of work in 4s, what is its useful power output in W?

5 A motor has a useful power output of 3 kW.

  a What is its useful power output in W?

  b How much useful work does it do in 1s?

  c If the power input to the motor is 4 kW, what is the efficiency?

6 Someone hauls a load weighing 600N through a vertical height of 10m in 20s.

  a How much useful work does she do?

  b How much useful work does she do in 1s?

  c What is her useful power output?

7 Human 'engines' (muscles) have an efficiency of about 15%. Explain why you must get hot when you exercise.

Energy for electricity (1)

A coal-burning power station. The large, round towers with clouds of steam coming from them are cooling towers.

Industrial societies use huge amounts of energy. Much of it is supplied by mains electricity. This comes from **generators** in **power stations**.

Thermal power stations

Power stations which use heat from a fuel to supply their energy are called **thermal power stations**. The diagram below shows the basic layout of a large thermal power station:

burning fuel:
coal
oil
natural gas

or
nuclear reactor

heat source   **boiler**

high-pressure steam

water

(condensed steam)

turbines   **generators**

cables

The generators are turned by **turbines**, blown round by high-pressure steam. To produce the steam, water is heated in a boiler. The heat comes from burning fuel (coal, oil, or natural gas) or from a **nuclear reactor**. Nuclear fuel does not burn. Its energy is released by nuclear reactions that split uranium atoms.

Once steam has passed through the turbines, it is cooled, condensed (turned back into a liquid), and fed back to the boiler.

To condense the steam, some power stations have huge cooling towers, with draughts of air up through them, as in the photograph above. Others use the cooling effect of nearby sea or river water.

Questions

1 Write down *four* types of fuel used in thermal power stations.

2 Give one type of thermal power station that does not burn its fuel.

Efficiency problems

Thermal power stations waste more energy than they deliver. Most is lost as heat in the cooling water and waste gases. For example, the efficiency of a typical coal-burning power station is only about 35% – only about 35% of the energy in its fuel is changed into electrical energy. You can see what happens to the rest in the chart below.

Engineers try to make power stations as efficient as they can. But it is impossible to use all of the heat from the fuel to produce motion. Petrol and diesel engines have the same problem.

The heat from a power station does not all have to be wasted. With long water pipes, some can be used to heat local buildings.

A turbine from a power station.

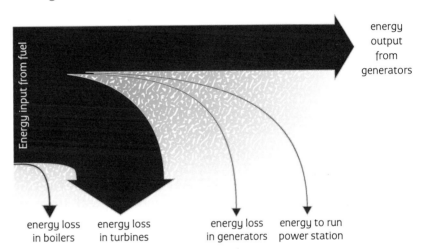

*What happens to the energy in a large thermal power station. The thicker the arrow, the greater the energy. An energy flow chart like this is called a **Sankey diagram**.*

Questions

3 In a thermal power station:

a Where does the steam come from?

b What is the steam used for?

c What turns the generators?

d What do the cooling towers do?

4 The table on the right gives data about the power input and losses in two power stations, X and Y:

a Where is most energy wasted?

b In what form is this wasted energy lost?

c What is the electrical power output of each station? (Assume that the table shows *all* the power losses in each station.)

d Which station has the higher efficiency?

	Power station	
	X	Y
	coal	nuclear
power input from fuel in MW	5600	5600
power losses in MW:		
– in reactors/boilers	600	200
– in turbines	2900	3800
– in generators	40	40
power to run station in MW	60	60
electrical power output in MW	?	?

Energy for electricity (2)

Objectives

This spread should help you to

- describe the problems caused by the use of fuel-burning and nuclear power stations
- describe how electricity can be generated using moving water and wind

Pollution problems

fuel (coal, oil, or natural gas)

oxygen (from air)

BURNING

carbon dioxide

water vapour

other gases

One effect of acid rain.

We would find it difficult to exist without electricity, but the power stations that supply it cause pollution. Fuel-burning power stations produce waste gases, as shown above. Nuclear power stations don't burn their fuel, but they produce radioactive waste.

- Fuel-burning power stations put carbon dioxide gas into the atmosphere. The carbon dioxide traps the Sun's energy and may be adding to **global warming**.
- Coal-burning power stations also produce sulphur dioxide gas. This causes **acid rain**, which damages stonework. One solution is to burn expensive low-sulphur coal. Another is to fit costly **flue gas desulphurization** (**FGD**) units to the power stations.
- Transporting fuels can cause pollution. For example, there may be a leak from an oil tanker at sea.
- The radioactive waste from nuclear power stations is highly dangerous. It must be carried away and stored safely in sealed containers for many years – in some cases, thousands of years.
- Nuclear accidents are rare. But when they do occur, radioactive gas and dust can be carried thousands of kilometres by winds.

If a tanker runs aground and leaks oil, the effects on the coast and its wildlife can be devastating.

Power from water and wind

Some generators are turned by the force of moving water or wind. Power schemes like this have no fuel costs, and give off no polluting gases. However, they can be expensive to build, and need large areas of land.

Hydroelectric power scheme *Rivers and rainwater fill up a lake behind a dam. As water rushes down from the dam, it turns turbines which turn generators.*

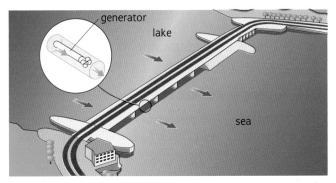

Tidal power scheme *A dam is built across a river where it meets the sea. The lake behind the dam fills when the tide comes in and empties when the tide goes out. The flow of water turns the generators.*

Wind farm *This is a collection of **aerogenerators** – generators driven by giant wind turbines ('windmills').*

Questions

1 Write down *three* types of power station that do *not* burn fuel.

2 Fuel-burning power stations give off carbon dioxide gas. What problem is caused by putting this gas into the atmosphere?

3 Describe how the generators are turned in a hydroelectric power scheme.

4 What are *aerogenerators*?

5 Coal-burning power stations also produce sulphur dioxide.

a What is the effect of putting this gas into the atmosphere?

b How can the amount of sulphur dioxide be reduced?

6 Nuclear power stations don't add to global warming.

a Why don't they add to global warming?

b Give *two* reasons why especially high safety standards are needed in nuclear power stations.

Energy resources

industry 35% domestic 30%

transport 20% other 15%

How energy is used in the UK.

Industrial societies need energy. Most comes from fuels which are burned in power stations, factories, homes, and vehicles.

Energy resources can be **renewable** or **non-renewable**. For example, wood is a renewable fuel. Once used, more can be grown to replace it. But oil is non-renewable. It took millions of years to form in the ground. Once used, it cannot be replaced.

Non-renewable energy resources

Fossil fuels Coal, oil, and natural gas are called fossil fuels because they formed from the remains of plants and tiny sea creatures which lived millions of years ago.

Problems Supplies are limited. When the fuels burn, their waste gases cause pollution. Carbon dioxide adds to global warming.

Nuclear fuels Most contain uranium. 1 kg of nuclear fuel stores as much energy as 25 tonnes of coal.

Problems Nuclear power stations are expensive to build, and expensive to close down when old. Their nuclear waste is dangerous and can stay radioactive for thousands of years.

Renewable energy resources

Hydroelectric energy A river fills a lake behind a dam. Water flowing down from the lake turns generators.

Problems Expensive to build. Few areas of the world are suitable. Flooding land and building a dam causes environmental damage.

Tidal energy Similar to hydroelectric energy, but a lake fills when the tide comes in and empties when it goes out.

Problems As for hydroelectric energy.

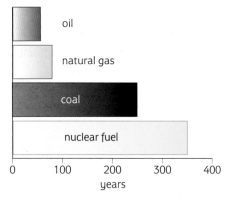

How long the world's known reserves of non-renewable fuels might last at present rates of consumption.

The world has a huge demand for oil, and oil companies are constantly looking for new reserves.

Did you know?
Nearly all of the world's energy originally came from the Sun. To find out how, look at the chart on the next spread.

Wind energy Generators are driven by wind turbines ('windmills').

Problems Large, remote, windy sites are needed. Winds are variable. The wind turbines are noisy, and spoil the landscape.

Wave energy Generators are driven by the up-and-down motion of waves at sea.

Problems Difficult to build – few devices have been successful.

Geothermal energy Steam comes from hot springs. Or water is pumped down to hot rocks deep underground and rises as steam.

Problems Deep drilling is difficult and expensive.

Solar energy **Solar panels** absorb radiated energy from the Sun and use it to heat water. **Solar cells** produce electricity.

Problems Variable amounts of sunshine. Solar cells are expensive.

Biofuels These are fuels made from plant or animal matter, sometimes called **biomass**. They include wood, alcohol made from sugar cane, and methane gas from rotting waste.

Problems Huge areas of land are needed to grow plants.

These solar cells deliver a current when sunlight falls on them.

Saving energy

Burning fossil fuels causes pollution. But the alternatives can also cause problems for the environment. That is why many people think that we should be less wasteful with energy. Methods include using public transport and bicycles instead of cars, putting better insulation in buildings, manufacturing goods that last longer, and recycling more of our waste materials.

Questions

You may need information from the chart in the next spread.

1 Some energy resources are *non-renewable*. What does this mean? Give *two* examples.

2 Give *two* ways of generating electricity in which no fuel is burned and the energy is renewable.

3 The energy in petrol originally came from the Sun. Explain how it got into the petrol.

4 What are *biofuels*? Give *two* examples.

5 Give *two* of the problems with relying on fossil fuels.

6 Look at the pie-charts on the right.

    a Which region has the largest oil reserves?

b What other fuel does this region have big reserves of?

c Which regions do you think might use most oil? Why?

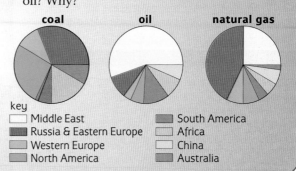

coal   oil   natural gas

key
- Middle East
- Russia & Eastern Europe
- Western Europe
- North America
- South America
- Africa
- China
- Australia

Solar panels

These absorb energy radiated from the Sun and use it to heat water.

Solar cells

These use the energy in sunlight to produce small amounts of electricity.

Energy in food

We get energy from the food we eat. The food may be from plants, or from animals which fed on plants.

Biofuels from plants

Wood is still an important fuel in many countries. When wood is burnt, it releases energy which the tree took in from the Sun. In some countries, sugar cane is grown and fermented to make alcohol. This can be used as a fuel instead of petrol.

Biofuels from waste

Rotting animal and plant waste can give off methane gas (as in natural gas). This can be used as a fuel. Marshes, rubbish tips, and sewage treatment works are all sources of methane. Some waste can also be used directly as fuel by burning it.

Batteries

Some batteries (for instance car batteries) have to be given energy by charging them with electricity. Others are manufactured from chemicals which already store energy. But energy is needed to produce the chemical in the first place.

The Sun

The Sun radiates energy because of nuclear reactions deep inside it. Its output is equivalent to 400 million billion billion electric hotplates! Just a tiny fraction reaches the Earth.

Energy in Plants

Plants take in energy from sunlight falling on their leaves. They use it to turn water and carbon dioxide from the air into new growth. Animals eat plants to get the energy stored in them.

Fossil fuels

Oil, natural gas, and coal are called fossil fuels. They were formed from the remains of plants and tiny sea creatures which lived many millions of years ago. Industrial societies rely on fossil fuels for most of their energy. Many power stations burn fossil fuels.

Fuels from oil

Many fuels can be extracted from oil. These include: petrol, diesel fuel, jet fuel, paraffin, central heating oil, bottled gas.

The Moon

The gravitational pull of the Moon (and to a lesser extent, the Sun) creates gentle bulges in the Earth's oceans. As the Earth rotates, different places have high and low tides as they pass in and out of the bulges. The motion of the tides carries energy with it.

Tidal energy

In a tidal energy scheme, an estuary is dammed to form an artificial lake.
Incoming tides fill the lake; outgoing tides empty it. The flow of water in and out of the lake turns generators.

Nucleus of the atom

Radioactive materials have atoms with unstable nuclei (centres) which break up and release energy. The material gives off the energy slowly as thermal energy. With some nuclei, energy can be released much more quickly by nuclear reactions.

Nuclear energy

In a reactor, nuclear reactions release energy from the nuclei of uranium atoms.
This produces heat which is used to make steam for driving generators.

Geothermal energy

Deep underground, the rocks are hotter than they are on the surface. The heat comes from radioactive materials naturally present in the rocks. It can be used to make steam for heating buildings or driving generators.

Wind energy

For centuries, people have been using the power of the wind to move ships, pump water, and grind corn. Today, huge wind turbines are used to turn generators.

Weather systems

These are partly driven by energy radiated from the Sun. Heated air rising above the equator causes belts of wind around the Earth. Winds carry water vapour from the oceans and bring rain and snow.

Wave energy

Waves are caused by the wind (and partly by tides). Waves cause a rapid-up-and-down movement on the surface of the sea. This movement can be used to drive generators.

Hydroelectric energy

An artificial lake forms behind a dam. Water rushing down from this lake is used to turn generators. The lake is kept full by river water which once fell as rain or snow.

ESCAPING HEAT

Most houses waste energy. When it is cold outside, the biggest waste of energy is lost heat. This is how the heat escapes from a typical house.

30% walls

10% roof

15% windows

35% draughts and air changes

10% floor

New air for old

Stopping draughts and air changes saves most on the fuel bills. But it can put your health – and even your life – at risk. If rooms are tightly sealed, any oxygen used up isn't replaced. Also, harmful substances collect in the air.

radioactive radon gas seeping from bricks and ground

methanal fumes from chipboard furniture

cigarette smoke

nitrogen dioxide from gas cooker

carbon monoxide from gas fire

A room should have at least one complete change of air per hour. In a draughty house, there may be 15 or more. This is good for clearing the air, but it makes the house expensive to heat.

U-values

To calculate likely heat losses from a house, architects need to know the **U-values** of different materials. For example:

1 m²

heat flow 3.6 joules every second

U-value 3.6

1°C

0°C

A single-brick wall has a U-value of 3.6 W/(m² °C). This means that a square metre of the wall, with a 1°C temperature difference across it, will conduct heat at the rate of 3.6 joules per second.

The heat flow is greater if:

* the temperature difference is higher.
* the area is greater.
* the wall is thinner.

U-value	W/(m² °C)
single-brick wall	3.6
double wall, with air cavity	1.7
double wall, with insulating fibrewool in cavity	0.5
glass window, single layer	5.7
double-glazed window	2.7

The lower the U-value, the better the material is as an insulator.

Low-energy houses

wind generator to supply some electrical power

central sun patio with opening roof

30 cm thick insulation in roof, walls, and floors

solar panels to partly heat water

heat exchanger to absorb heat from outgoing stale air and pass it to incoming fresh air

small double-glazed windows

This is a design for a low-energy house. In winter, the power of a one-bar electric heater is enough to heat the whole house. The house is good for the environment – but, unfortunately, it is far too expensive for most people to buy. Also, there is one way in which it could be improved...

For the same level of insulation, a terraced house like the one on the right wastes less energy than other types. Sandwiched between other buildings, it has a smaller surface area for heat to escape to the outside.

Talking points

● **In cold conditions, most houses waste too much heat.**

❋ What causes the greatest loss of heat from a house?

❋ Why can it be dangerous to stop this loss completely?

● **Look at the table of U-values opposite.**

❋ Which will let most heat escape, a double wall with air cavity or a double-glazed window of the same area?

❋ Are houses with small windows likely to lose less heat than those with larger windows? Can you explain your answer?

Coping with COLD

WARM to the core COLD risks

In winter, someone's hands and feet may be cold, but they can cope with the harsh conditions outside, provided the temperature of their body's **core** doesn't drop below the normal 37 °C.

If the body loses too much heat, and its core temperature drops more than 2 °C, it stops working properly. The condition is called **hypothermia.**
Old people are at risk from hypothermia if their homes are not heated properly.

Exercise is a particularly good way of keeping warm. That is because the human body isn't very efficient as an 'engine'. For every joule of energy delivered by your muscles, your body must release about 6 joules from your food by 'burning' it. The other 5 joules warm you up!

Young babies also find it difficult to cope with the cold. They don't store as much body heat as adults, so any loss has a bigger effect. And they can't adjust to sudden heat losses because their temperature control system isn't fully developed.

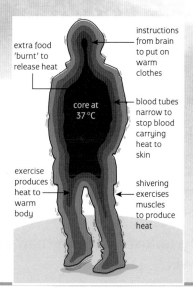

extra food 'burnt' to release heat

instructions from brain to put on warm clothes

core at 37 °C

blood tubes narrow to stop blood carrying heat to skin

exercise produces heat to warm body

shivering exercises muscles to produce heat

How the body keeps warm.

Reducing radiation

These shiny capes help keep marathon runners warm when the race is over.

Survival at sea

If the windsurfer in the photo gets in the water without an insulating suit, he could be suffering from hypothermia in minutes. In a cold sea, the human body loses heat over 20 times faster than in cold air.

A wet-suit is worn with a layer of water trapped between the suit and the diver's skin. The water is an insulator. More insulation comes from the thousands of tiny nitrogen bubbles trapped in the suit's lining.

Polar lifestyle

With lots of fur to trap air, and layers of thick fat under the skin for extra insulation, a polar bear has no problems retaining body heat. Even a swim in icy water can seem quite pleasant if there's a chance of catching a meal at the same time.

Talking points

Can you suggest a reason for each of the following?

* Exercise warms you up.

* Old people are more at risk from hypothermia than younger people.

* Marathon runners may put on a shiny cape when the race is over.

* The changing room at a swimming pool is kept at a temperature of 25 °C, but the pool itself is kept at 30 °C.

1 The diagram below shows a model power-station. A small steam engine drives a generator which lights a bulb. Decide where each of the following energy changes is taking place. (You can answer by writing one of the letters A–D in each case.)

steam engine
B
A
burning fuel
C
bulb
D
generator

a Kinetic energy to electrical energy.

b Heat energy to kinetic energy.

c Electrical energy to heat and light energy.

d Chemical energy to heat energy.

2 A skier is pulled up a slope by holding a handle attached to a moving cable. The skier rises through a vertical height of 100 m in 5 mins. If the skier weighs 600 N.

a Calculate the energy spent in lifting the skier to the top of the slope.

b Assuming the system is 100% efficient calculate the power of the system.

c Suggest two reasons why the system will not be 100% efficient.

3 Some workers on a building site have set up an electric winch in order to lift a bucket with tiles up to the roof. If the bucket and tiles weigh 500 N

a What is the minimum force that must be applied in order to lift the bucket of tiles off the ground?

b How much energy is spent in lifting the tiles 20 m from the ground to the roof?

c What energy transformations are taking place as the tiles are raised?

d If the tiles are lifted 20 m in 10 s, what is the power of the winch?

e If the winch is only 50% efficient, how much energy must be fed into the electrical motor to lift the tiles the 20 m?

f Suggest one or two reasons why the system might be less than 100% efficient.

g How can the efficiency of the system be improved?

4 An isolated village uses solar panels and windmills as energy sources.

windmills
power lines
solar panels

a i Write down one **advantage** of using these energy sources.

ii Write down one **disadvantage** of using solar panels.

iii Write down one **disadvantage** of using windmills.

5 The diagram below shows a hydroelectric scheme. Water rushes down from the top of the lake to the power-station. In the power-station, the water turns a turbine which drives a generator.

lake
dam
15 m
power-station

a What type of energy does the water have when it reaches the power-station?

b Some of the water's energy is wasted.

i Why is energy wasted?

ii What happens to the wasted energy?

6 The hydroelectric scheme in question 5 is a renewable energy resource.

a What is meant by a *renewable energy resource*?

b When water flows from the lake, potential energy is lost. How is this energy replaced?

c What advantages does a hydroelectric scheme have over a fuel-burning power-station?

d What environmental damage does a hydroelectric scheme cause?

7 At night time when most of us are asleep the demand for electricity is quite small. The generators at the power stations, however, are still working as it is very wasteful and inefficient to turn them off. In some power stations the excess electrical energy they are manufacturing is used to pump water uphill into dams. Then during the day the water is released and used to drive generators when demand is high.

a What weight of water can be pumped 50 m uphill if the surplus energy from a generator is 2 MJ?

b When released, how much kinetic energy will this water have after it has fallen

i 25 m?

ii 50 m?

What assumptions have you made?

c If the generator driven by the water is only 40% efficient, how much energy is lost?

d Suggest why off-peak night-time electricity is cheaper than daytime electricity.

8 To be a good pole vaulter it is essential not only to be strong and agile but also to have good sprinting speed.

a What kind of energy does a vaulter possess

i before starting his run?

ii as he sprints down the runway?

iii as he clears the bar?

b When a competitor has completed his vault where has all the energy gone?

9 On the motorway, some road signs are powered by batteries. The batteries are recharged by solar cells.

a What is the energy source for **solar** cells?

b For every 100 J of energy supplied to the sign by the batteries, the sign produces 80 J of useful energy.

i What type of energy does the other 20 J become?

ii Use the formula

$$\text{efficiency} = \frac{\text{useful energy output}}{\text{total energy input}} \times 100\%$$

to calculate the efficiency of the road sign.

10 The diagram below shows a power station which supplies the National Grid.

a What is the National Grid?

b Most power stations use fossil fuels as their energy source. The table below shows how long some energy sources will last if they are used at the present rate.

energy source	time in years
oil	40
natural gas	60
coal	220

i Which source will be used up first?

ii Suggest **two** reasons why the energy sources might last **longer** than the table says.

11 The table below gives information about some of the energy sources that are used to generate electricity in the United Kingdom.

Energy source	Renewable	Known world reserves	Efficiency of electricity production
coal	no	200 years	40%
oil	no	40 years	35%
gas	no	65 years	50%
wind	yes	none	40%

a i Which of these energy sources are fossil fuels?

ii Which fossil fuel has the largest known reserves?

iii Which fossil fuel is used most efficiently to produce electricity?

iv Why is wind described as renewable?

b Suggest TWO reasons why only a small proportion of our electricity is generated from wind.

c Explain why it is important to develop renewable energy sources.

12 In sunny countries, some houses have a solar heater on the roof. It warms up water for the house. The diagram below shows a typical arrangement.

a Why is the panel in the solar heater black?

b Why is there an insulating layer behind the panel?

c How does the water in the tank get heated?

d Why does the solar panel work best if placed at an angle, rather than flat or upright?

e On average, each square metre of the solar panel above receives 1000 joules of energy from the Sun every second. Use this figure to calculate the power input (in kW) of the panel if its surface area is 2 m².

f The solar heater in the diagram has an efficiency of 60% (it wastes 40% of the solar energy it receives). What area of panel would be needed to deliver heat at the same rate, on average, as a 3 kW electric immersion heater?

g i What are the advantages of using a solar heater instead of an immersion heater?

ii What are the disadvantages?

13 The diagram below shows a section through a radiator.

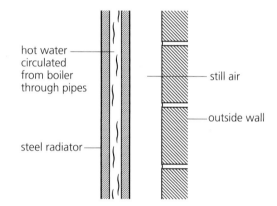

Describe, as fully as you can, how heat from inside the radiator travels out into the room.

Why would a sheet of silver foil placed on the surface of the wall prevent some of the heat from escaping to the outside?

14 The diagram below shows a hot-water storage tank. The water is heated by an electric immersion heater at the bottom.

a How could heat loss from the tank be reduced? What materials would be suitable for the job?

b Why is the heater placed at the bottom of the tank rather than the top?

c The heater has a power output of 3kW.

   i What does the 'k' stand for in 'kW'?

   ii How many joules of heat energy does the heater deliver in one second?

   iii How many joules of heat energy does the heater deliver in 7 minutes?

15 The diagram below shows how much heat might escape from a house if there was no insulation.

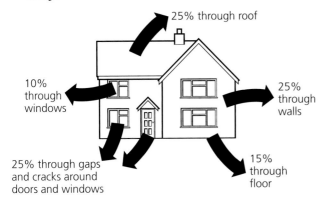

25% through roof

10% through windows

25% through walls

25% through gaps and cracks around doors and windows

15% through floor

Suggest 5 methods of reducing the loss of heat from this house.

16 The diagram below shows a refrigerator. In and around a refrigerator, heat is transferred by conduction, by convection, and by evaporation. Decide which process is mainly responsible for the heat transfer in each of the following:

refrigerant (vapour)

freezer compartment

refrigerant (liquid)

cooling fins

a Cool air descending from the freezer compartment takes away heat from the food.

b Heat is lost to the outside air through the cooling fins at the back.

c Some heat from the kitchen enters the refrigerator through its outer panels.

d Some heat enters the refrigerator every time the door is opened.

Key words

The spread numbers in brackets tell you where to find more information.

conductor (thermal) A material that lets heat (thermal energy) flow through it. Metals are the best conductors. *(6.04)*

convection Process in which heat (thermal energy) is carried by a circulating flow of liquid or gas (air, for example). *(6.04)*

efficiency If an engine or motor has an efficiency of 0.25 (25%), only a quarter of the energy supplied to it is delivered as work (useful energy output). The rest is wasted. *(6.06)*

energy Things have energy if they can be used to do work – in other words, to make forces move. Energy is measured in joules (J). *(6.01)*

insulator (thermal) A material that is a very poor conductor of heat (thermal energy). *(6.04)*

joule (J) Unit of energy and work. 1000 joules equals 1 kilojoule (kJ). *(6.01)*

kinetic energy The energy something has because of its motion. *(6.01, 6.03)*

potential energy The energy something has because of a change in position or shape. *(6.01, 6.03)*

power The rate at which work is done or energy is transformed (changed into another form). It is measured in watts (W). 1 watt is equal to 1 joule per second. *(6.06, 2.09)*

radiation (thermal) Rays, such as those from the Sun, that have a heating effect when something absorbs them. The rays are mostly infrared. *(6.05)*

turbine A wheel with blades which are pushed round by steam, gas, or water. In power stations, the generators are turned by turbines. *(6.07)*

watt (W) Unit of power. It is equal to 1 joule per second. *(2.09, 6.06)*

work Work is done whenever a force makes something move. 1 joule (J) of work is done when a force of 1 newton moves something a distance of 1 metre (in the direction of the force). *(6.01)*

Magnets and currents

At night, a city like this is bright enough to be seen from space. Modern industrial societies rely heavily on the use of electricity – not only for lighting, as above, but also for running factory machinery, information and communications systems, and heating. Typically, about one sixth of our energy is delivered by electricity. It comes from huge generators in power stations.

Magnets and fields

A suspended bar magnet will turn so that it points roughly north–south.

Poles of a magnet

If a small bar magnet is dipped into iron filings, the filings cling to its ends, as shown on the right. The magnetic forces seem to come from two points, called the **poles** of the magnet.

The Earth pulls on the poles of a magnet. If a bar magnet is suspended, as on the left, it turns until it lies roughly north–south. Because of this effect, the two poles of a magnet are called:

- the north-seeking pole (or N pole for short)
- the south-seeking pole (or S pole for short)

If the ends of similar magnets are brought together, as below:

> Like poles repel. Unlike poles attract.
> The closer the poles, the greater the force between them.

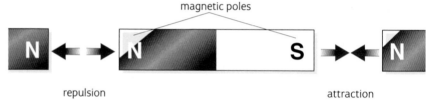

repulsion   attraction

Permanent and temporary magnets

Pieces of iron and steel *become* magnets if placed near a magnet. The magnet **induces** magnetism in the two metals. It attracts them because the poles nearest each other are different.

When the pieces of metal are pulled away, the steel keeps its magnetism, but the iron does not. The steel has become a **permanent magnet**. The iron was only a **temporary magnet**.

Iron filings are attracted to the poles of a magnet.

Materials which can be magnetized and are attracted to magnets are called **magnetic materials**. All strongly magnetic materials contain iron, nickel, or cobalt. For example, steel is mainly iron.

Field around a magnet

A magnet has a **magnetic field** in the space around it. In this space, there are forces on any magnetic material there.

You can study the field using a small **compass**, as below. The 'needle' is a tiny magnet which is free to turn on its spindle. The forces from the poles of the magnet make it line up with the field.

The Earth is a weak magnet. Its field will turn a compass needle – or any suspended magnet – so that it points roughly north–south.

What happens when iron filings are sprinkled onto a piece of acetate over a bar magnet. The filings have become tiny magnets, pulled into position by forces from the poles of the magnet. Their pattern shows what the **magnetic field** around the magnet is like.

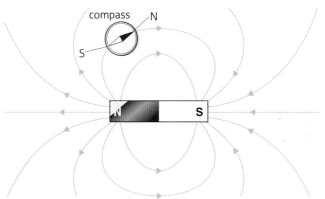

The field around a magnet can be shown using magnetic **field lines**. These run from the N pole to the S pole of the magnet. They show the direction in which the N end of a compass needle would point. The magnetic field is strongest where the field lines are closest together.

Questions

1 Why are the poles of a magnet called N and S?

2 What type of magnetic pole:
  a attracts an N pole? **b** repels an S pole?

3 How can you show that there is a field around a magnet?

4 In the diagram on the right, pieces of iron and steel are being attracted to the end of a magnet.
  a Copy the diagram. Draw in any magnetic poles on the iron and steel.
  b If the lower ends of the iron and steel start to move, which way will they move, and why?

c What happens to each of the metals when it is taken away from the magnet?

Magnetism from currents

Objectives

This spread should help you to

• describe how a current in a wire or coil produces a magnetic field

Magnetic field around a wire

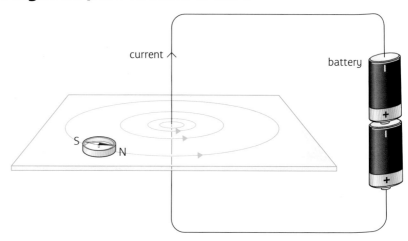

If a current is passed through a wire, as shown above, it produces a weak magnetic field. The field has these features:

• The magnetic field lines are in circles.
• The field is strongest close to the wire.
• If you increase the current, this makes the field stronger.
• If you reverse the current direction, this reverses the field.

A rule for field direction Imagine gripping the wire with your *right* hand so that your thumb points the same way as the current (see left). Your fingers then point in the same direction as the field lines.

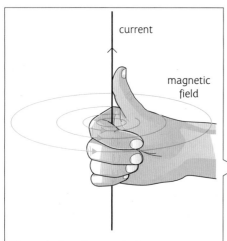

The right-hand grip rule for magnetic field direction.

Magnetic field from a coil

A current produces a stronger magnetic field if the wire is wound into a coil. The diagram below shows the magnetic field around a current-carrying coil. A long coil like this is called a **solenoid**.

Did you know?

Use the right directions!

When using the rules described on this spread, remember:

• The current direction is from the + terminal of a battery round to the –.

• The magnetic field direction is the direction the N end of a compass needle would point.

The right-hand grip rule for magnetic poles.

When you record a TV programme, a tiny current-carrying coil puts magnetic patterns on the tape.

The magnetic field produced by a coil has these features:

- The field is like that around a bar magnet, with magnetic poles at the ends of the coil.
- If you increase the current, this makes the field stronger.
- If you put more turns on the coil, the field is stronger.
- If you reverse the current direction, this reverses the field.

A rule for poles Imagine gripping the coil with your *right* hand so that your fingers point the same way as the current (left). Your thumb then points towards the N pole of the coil.

Making magnets

Below, a steel bar is in a solenoid. When a current is passed through the solenoid, the steel becomes magnetized, and makes the magnetic field much stronger than before.

When the current through the solenoid is switched off, the steel stays magnetized. Nearly all permanent magnets are made in this way, using pulses of very high current.

In audio and video cassette recorders, tiny current-carrying coils are used to put magnetic patterns on tape. The patterns store sound and picture information.

Questions

1 In diagram **A** on the right, the coil is producing a magnetic field.

  a Give *two* ways in which the strength of the field could be increased.

  b How could the direction of the field be reversed?

  c If you had a steel rod, how could you use a coil like this to make it into a magnet?

2 Diagram **B** shows the end view of a long wire with four compasses around it. If a high current is passed through the wire, needle X doesn't move. Redraw the diagram to show how the other compass needles will point.

Objectives

This spread should help you to

- explain how electromagnets work
- describe some uses of electromagnets

An **electromagnet** can do all the things that an ordinary magnet can do, but you can switch it on and off. The one in the photograph above is being used to pick up scrap iron and then drop it.

The diagram below shows a simple electromagnet:

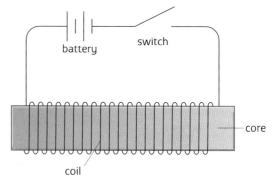

An electromagnet has these parts:

A **coil** made from several hundred turns of insulated copper wire. The more turns there are, the stronger the magnetic field.

A **battery** to supply current. The higher the current, the stronger the magnetic field. If you reverse the current, this reverses the direction of the field.

A **core** made from iron or Mumetal. This makes the field about a thousand times stronger than the coil by itself. Its magnetism dies away as soon as the current is switched off. (Steel would not be suitable as a core because it would stay magnetized.)

The devices on the next page contain electromagnets.

Questions

1 Why should the core of an electromagnet be made of iron rather than steel?

2 Describe *two* changes you could make to give an electromagnet a stronger pull.

3 What change would you have to make to reverse the direction of the magnetic field from an electromagnet?

The magnetic relay

With a relay, a small switch with thin wires can be used to turn on the current in a much more powerful circuit – for example, one with a large electric motor in it:

With a relay, a small switch can be used to turn on a powerful starter motor.

When you close switch S in the input circuit, a current flows through the electromagnet, and pulls the iron lever towards it, closing contacts C. So current flows through the motor.

The circuit breaker

A circuit breaker cuts off the current in a circuit if this gets too high. It has the same effect as a fuse but, unlike a fuse, can be reset (turned ON again) after it has tripped (turned OFF).

Some houses have circuit breakers in the 'fuse box', rather than fuses.

The current flows through two contacts and an electromagnet. If it gets too high, the pull of the electromagnet becomes strong enough to release the iron catch, so the contacts open and stop the current. Pressing the reset button closes them again.

Questions

4 In the diagram at the top of the page, an electric motor is controlled by a switch connected to a relay.

  a What is the advantage of using a relay, rather than a switch in the motor circuit itself?

  b Why does the motor start when switch S is closed?

5 The diagram above shows a circuit breaker.

  a What is the purpose of the circuit breaker?

  b What advantage does a circuit breaker have compared with a fuse?

  c How do you think the performance of the circuit breaker would be affected if the coil of the electromagnet had more turns?

Magnets, motion, and motors (1)

Magnets don't only push and pull on other magnets and magnetic materials. Their fields also have an effect on an electric current. This idea is used in electric motors, loudspeakers, and meters.

In the diagram below left, a wire has been placed between the poles of a magnet. When a current flows through the wire, there is an upward force on it.

The force becomes stronger if you do the following:

- Increase the current.
- Use a stronger magnet.
- Increase the length of wire in the field.

If you reverse either the current or the field, the force is reversed. If the wire is in line with the field, there isn't any force at all.

Fleming's left-hand rule.

Fleming's left-hand rule

This is a rule for working out the direction of the force when the current is at right-angles to the magnetic field.

The rule is shown above. It works like this:

Hold the thumb and first two fingers of your left hand at right-angles. If you point your fingers as shown above, your thumb gives the direction of the force.

When you use the rule, remember these points:

- The current direction is from + to –.
- The field lines run from N to S.

Questions

1 In the diagram above, what would happen if:

   a the current was increased?

   b the direction of the current was reversed?

A moving-coil loudspeaker.

The needle of this meter is moved by a coil which turns in a magnetic field when a current flows through it.

Moving-coil loudspeaker

In the loudspeaker on the left, the magnet is specially shaped so that the wire of the coil is at right-angles to its field. The coil can move in and out. It is attached to a cone made of stiff paper or plastic.

The loudspeaker is connected to an amplifier which gives out an alternating current. This flows backwards and forwards through the wire, causing a force which pushes the coil in and out. So the cone vibrates. And as it vibrates, it gives out sound waves.

Turning effect on a coil

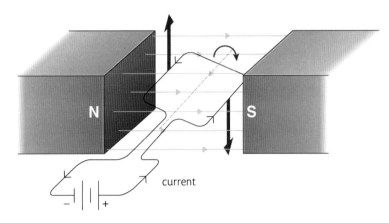

The coil above lies between the poles of a magnet. The current flows in opposite directions along the two sides of the coil. So one side is pushed *up* and the other side is pushed *down*. In other words, there is a turning effect on the coil. With more turns on the coil, the turning effect is stronger. The turning effect is used in electric motors and some meters.

Questions

2 In the diagram on the right, there is a force on the wire.
   a Give *two* ways in which the force could be increased.
   b Give *two* ways in which the direction of the force could be reversed.

3 Explain why the cone of a loudspeaker vibrates if alternating current is passed through its coil.

4 The diagram above shows a current-carrying coil in a magnetic field. What difference would it make if:
   a there were more turns of wire in the coil?
   b the direction of the current were reversed?

Magnets, motion, and motors (2)

A simple d.c. motor

The motor below runs on direct current (d.c.), the 'one-way' current that flows from a battery. It uses the idea that a magnetic field can have a turning effect on a coil with a current in it.

The coil is made of insulated copper wire. It is free to rotate between the poles of the magnet. The **commutator**, or split ring, is fixed to the coil and rotates with it. The **brushes** are two contacts which rub against the commutator and keep the coil connected to the battery. They are usually made of carbon.

magnet

coil

N

S

commutator (split ring)

brushes

battery

The two forces above can't pull the coil beyond the vertical position, because they are then pointing the wrong way. The commutator solves this problem with a clever trick: as the coil shoots past the vertical, the commutator *reverses* the current direction. Now the forces point the other way, so the coil is pulled round another half turn... and so on. In this way, the coil keeps rotating.

For a stronger turning effect on the coil, you can:

- Increase the current.
- Use a stronger magnet.
- Put more turns on the coil.
- Use a bigger coil.

Questions

1 Which part(s) of an electric motor:
   a connect the power supply to the split ring and coil?
   b changes the current direction every half turn?

iron or Mumetal

Practical motors have several coils, wound on iron or Mumetal.

Practical motors

Practical motors have several coils set at different angles, each with their own pair of commutator segments (pieces), as shown on the left. The coils are wound on iron or Mumetal to guide the field. These features give smoother running and a greater turning effect.

Some motors use electromagnets rather than permanent magnets. This means that they can run on alternating current (a.c.). As the current flows backwards and forwards through the coil, the field from the electromagnet changes direction to match it, so the turning effect is always the same way. The mains motors in drills and food mixers work like this.

The motors in CD players and in some industrial machines don't have commutators and moving coils. They work on a different principle: the forces are generated by a changing magnetic field.

In this electric drill, the motor is at the right-hand end. Note the commutator segments and the electromagnet.

Questions

2 On the right, there is an end view of the coil in a simple electric motor.

   a Why is there an upward force on one side of the coil, but a downward force on the other?

   b Give *two* ways in which the turning effect on the coil could be increased.

   c Describe *two* things you could change in order to make the motor run backwards.

3 What is the advantage of using an electromagnet in an electric motor, rather than a permanent magnet?

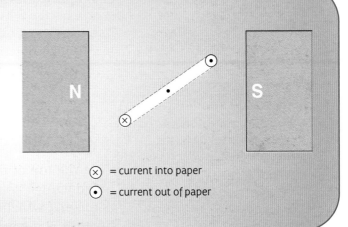

⊗ = current into paper

⊙ = current out of paper

Electricity from magnetism

You don't need batteries to produce a current: just a wire, a magnet, and movement.

Generating a voltage in a wire

If you move a wire across a magnetic field, as shown below left, a small voltage is generated in the wire. The effect is called **electromagnetic induction**. Scientifically speaking, a voltage is **induced** in the wire. As the wire is part of a complete circuit, the voltage makes a current flow.

induced current — sensitive meter

greater induced current

insulated wire

To increase the induced voltage (and current), you can:

- Move the wire faster.
- Use a stronger magnet.
- Increase the length of wire in the field – for example, by looping the wire through the field several times, as shown above right.

These results are summed up by **Faraday's law**, given here in simplified form:

> Whenever a conductor cuts through magnetic field lines, a voltage is generated. The faster the field lines are cut, the greater the voltage. If no field lines are cut there is no voltage.

Generating a voltage in a coil

At the top of the next page, you can see another way of inducing a voltage (and current) in a wire. This time, it is the magnet which is being moved rather than the wire. But the result is the same: field lines are being cut.

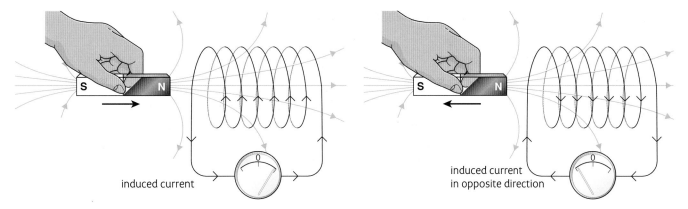

induced current

induced current in opposite direction

To increase the induced voltage (and current), you can:

- Move the magnet faster.
- Use a stronger magnet.
- Put more turns on the coil.

If you pull the magnet *out of* the coil, as shown above right, the direction of the induced voltage (and current) is reversed. Turning the magnet round, so that the S pole goes in and out, rather than the N pole, also reverses the current direction. If you hold the magnet still, no field lines are cut, so there is no induced voltage or current.

Guitar pick-ups are tiny coils with magnets inside them. The magnets magnetize the steel strings. When the strings vibrate, current is induced in the coils, boosted by an amplifier, and used to produce sound.

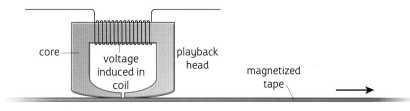

core

voltage induced in coil

playback head

magnetized tape

The playback heads in audio and video cassette recorders contain tiny coils. A tiny, varying voltage is induced (generated) in the coil as the magnetized tape passes over it. In this way, the magnetized patterns on the tape are changed into electrical signals. These are amplified and used to reproduce the original sound or picture.

Questions

2 In the experiment on the opposite page, a current is being induced in a wire. What would be the effect of:

a using a stronger magnet?

b moving the wire faster?

c moving the wire along the magnetic field lines instead of across them?

3 In the experiment at the top of the page, what would be the effect of:

a moving the magnet faster?

b turning the magnet round, so that the S pole is pushed into the coil?

c putting more turns on the coil?

Generators and transformers

Most of our electricity comes from huge **generators** in power stations. There are smaller generators in cars and motorcycles. All use electromagnetic induction. Most generate **alternating current (a.c.)**. These are also known as **alternators**.

A simple a.c. generator (alternator)

The alternator below is supplying current to a small bulb. The **coil** is rotated by turning the shaft. The **slip rings** rotate with the coil. The **brushes** are usually made of carbon. They rub against the slip rings and keep the coil connected to the outside part of the circuit.

A simple a.c. generator, connected to a bulb.

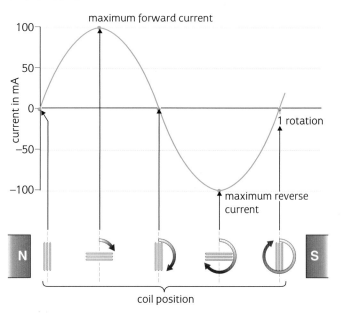

Graph showing the generator's a.c. output.

When the coil is rotated, it cuts magnetic field lines, so a voltage is generated. This makes a current flow. As the coil rotates, each side travels upwards, downwards, upwards, downwards... and so on, through the field. So the current flows backwards, forwards... and so on. In other words, it is a.c.

The voltage (and current) from the generator can be increased by:

- putting more turns on the coil.
- using a bigger coil.
- using a stronger magnet.
- rotating the coil faster.

Faster rotation increases the frequency of the a.c. Mains generators must keep a steady frequency: 50 Hz (cycles per second) in the UK.

Questions

1 What does an alternator do?
2 If the alternator above were given a stronger magnet, how would this affect its output?

An alternator in a car.

This power adaptor contains a step-down transformer to reduce the 230 volts from the mains to about 9 volts. (It also contains a rectifier to change the a.c. to d.c.)

Practical alternators

These usually have fixed coils arranged around a rotating electromagnet. This means that the current generated does not have to flow through sliding contacts, which might overheat.

Cars need 'one-way' direct current (d.c.) for recharging the battery and running other circuits. They use a device called a **rectifier** to change the alternator's a.c. output to d.c.

Transformers

transformer

An a.c. voltage can be changed using a **transformer** like the one above. The **primary coil** is used as an electromagnet. When connected to an a.c. supply, it produces an alternating magnetic field. This induces a voltage in the **secondary coil** – as would happen if you could move a magnet in and out of the coil very fast.

The output voltage depends on how many turns there are on each coil. For example, if the secondary coil has *half* the turns of the primary, the output voltage is *half* the input voltage. **Step-up transformers** increase voltage, **step-down transformers** reduce it.

Transformers don't give you something for nothing. If they *increase* voltage, they *decrease* the current, and vice versa.

Questions

3 Current can be a.c. or d.c.
  a What do a.c. and d.c. stand for?
  b Which type is generated by an alternator?
  c Which type is used by a transformer?

4 What job is done by:
  a a step-up transformer?
  b a step-down transformer?

5 Look at the simple alternator on the opposite page.
  a Why does this alternator need slip rings?
  b If the alternator were turned faster, how would its output change?
  c Most practical alternators have a different layout from the simple type shown. How are they different?
  d Why do some alternators have a rectifier fitted?

Power across the country

400 000 V

33 000 V

power station

transformer (step-up)

generation

transmission

Power for the alternating current (a.c.) mains is *generated* in power stations, *transmitted* (sent) through long-distance cables, and then *distributed* to consumers.

In a typical large power station, the generators are driven by huge turbines, spun round by the force of high-pressure steam. The steam is made by heating water in a boiler. The heat comes from burning coal, oil, or natural gas – or from a nuclear reactor.

The current from each generator is fed to a huge step-up transformer. This transfers power to overhead cables at greatly increased voltage (see the next page to find out why). The cables feed power to a nationwide supply network called the **Grid**. Using the Grid, power stations in areas where the demand is low can supply areas where the demand is high.

Power from the grid is distributed by a series of **substations**. These contain step-down transformers which reduce the voltage in stages to the level needed by consumers. In Europe, this is 230 volts (V) for home consumers, although industry usually gets a higher voltage.

Questions

1 *transmission*   *generation*
   distribution

   Which of the above words describes each of these?

   a Producing power in a power station.

   b Sending power across country.

A typical large power station might contain four generators like this, each producing a current of 20 000 amperes or more, at a voltage of 33 000 volts.

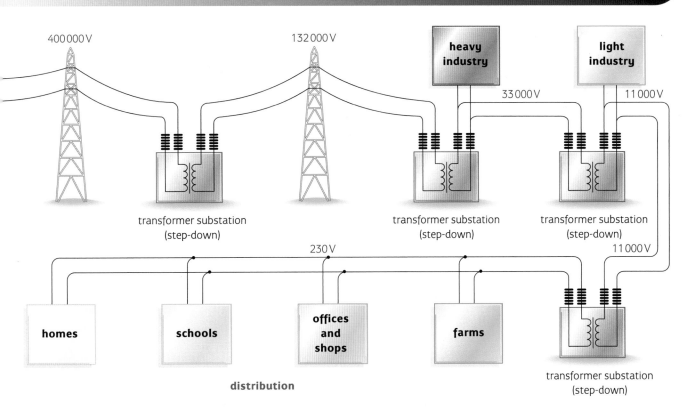

400 000 V   132 000 V

heavy industry

light industry

33 000 V   11 000 V

transformer substation (step-down)

transformer substation (step-down)

transformer substation (step-down)

11 000 V

230 V

11 000 V

homes

schools

offices and shops

farms

transformer substation (step-down)

distribution

Pylons and overhead cables are not usually allowed in areas like this.

Why use a.c.? The main advantage is that a.c. voltages can be stepped up or down using transformers. Transformers will not work with 'one-way' direct current (d.c.).

Why transmit at high voltage? Transmission cables waste energy because of the heating effect of the current. By using a transformer to *increase* the voltage, the current in the cables is *reduced*. This means that less energy is lost before it reaches the consumer.

Overhead or underground? Overhead cables are the cheapest way of sending power long distances. Underground cables are more expensive to lay. However, they are used in areas of outstanding natural beauty, where pylons would spoil the landscape.

Questions

2 a What is the *Grid*?

   b When supplying power to consumers, what is the main advantage of using the Grid?

3 What are transformers used for?

4 When power from generators is fed to overhead transmission cables, why is the voltage stepped up?

5 What are substations for?

6 What is the main advantage of using a.c. rather than d.c. for power transmission?

7 Give an example of where underground transmission cables might be used instead of overhead ones, despite the extra cost.

Guaranteed POWER

Power cuts don't happen very often. But when they do, the results can be serious:

If there is a loss of power in a dairy, two hundred cows will need milking by hand.

A loss of power in an operating theatre might put someone's life at risk.

For emergencies, most large hospitals and farms have stand-by generators. They are driven by engines which run on petrol, diesel, or bottled gas. They start up automatically if there is a mains failure.

Extra POWER

In Somerset, hens have solved one farmer's electricity supply problems. He saves their droppings in a tank, collects the gas given off, and uses it to run the engine for his generator.

In Florida, the police have collected so many drugs in raids that a power station has been converted to burn them. One tonne of marijuana gives nearly as much heat as three barrels of oil.

In Edmonton, North London, an Energy-From-Waste power station burns household rubbish as its fuel. It provides 32 megawatts of power for 24000 homes – and gets rid of the waste as well.

Turbo alternator

Electrical output to grid

Steam to turbines

Boiler

ESP

Waste input

Waste bunker

Flue gas treatment

Stack

Bag house filter

Ash recycling

Period of low demand

upper reservoir filling

water pumped up

motor–
generator

lower reservoir emptying

power in **pump–turbine**

Period of high demand

upper reservoir emptying

water flows down

motor–
generator

lower reservoir filling

power out pump–**turbine**

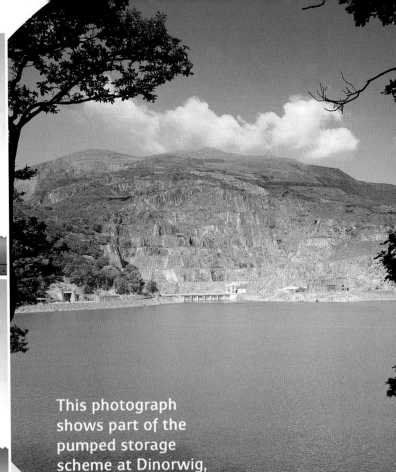

This photograph shows part of the pumped storage scheme at Dinorwig, North Wales

Pumped storage POWER

Generating companies have to meet a high demand for electricity during the day. But at night, costly generators may be lying idle. One way of reducing this problem is to use a **pumped storage scheme**. The diagrams above show the basic idea behind such a scheme.

When demand is low, spare power is used to pump water from the lower to the upper reservoir. When demand is high, the water is released so that it flows down to turn the generator. The equipment is cleverly designed so that the turbine can be reversed and used as a pump. And when the generator is *supplied* with current, it acts as a motor and drives the pump.

Talking points

Using the index, or other sources of information, see if you can find out:

- what fuels are normally used in power stations.

- what features electric motors and generators have in common.

Electricity supply companies have special departments which look ahead to find out when the most popular TV programmes are going to start and finish. Can you suggest reasons why?

Power for motion

Engines or motors?

The car above is good for special occasions, but not for parking in tight spaces or getting round corners. And it is certainly not good for the environment. The exhaust gases from its huge petrol engine pollute the atmosphere.

The car on the left is more cramped and not so good for long distances. But it is less polluting. It is powered by an electric motor, so it doesn't have an exhaust pipe. If everyone drove cars like this, conditions in city centres would be much more pleasant.

Electric motors are a clean and efficient way of turning the wheels. But present-day electric cars have one major problem. They need batteries. These are a relatively poor way of storing energy and must be recharged. Battery-powered cars will never have the performance or range of petrol or diesel models.

These can deliver the same amount of energy

1 full tank of petrol
mass: 50 kg
time to refill: 3 minutes

150 fully charged car batteries
mass: 1500 kg (1.5 tonnes)
time to recharge: 3 hours

Fuel cell future

Fortunately, there is a solution to the battery problem. It is a source of electricity called a **fuel cell**. When you feed a fuel cell with hydrogen (plus oxygen from the air), chemical reactions deliver a continuous supply of electricity. The cell doesn't need recharging. As long as you feed in the gases, the cell delivers the current, and the only waste product is water. Fuel cells have been around for years. However, the technology has only recently become cheap enough for cars.

In cars, the main problem with fuel cells is how to store the hydrogen. It isn't safe or practical to carry large cylinders of this highly inflammable gas. That is why the fuel in the tank is likely to be liquid methanol. A unit called a **reformer** produces hydrogen from the methanol using steam and catalysts.

Methanol, or 'wood alcohol', can be made using plant materials grown as a renewable resource. It can also be produced from natural gas. Vehicles with fuel cells will have the range and performance of today's fuel burners but be more efficient and less polluting. The days of petrol and diesel engines may soon be over.

An old problem

Pollution isn't a new problem. In the 1800s, horse-drawn traffic was increasing so much that it was estimated that, by the end of the century, Londoners would be up to their knees in horse manure.

Talking points

⚙️ Present-day electric cars have batteries which are recharged by plugging them in to a mains-powered charger. Their electric motors produce no pollution. Can you suggest reasons why, if everyone drove cars like this, the system would still cause atmospheric pollution?

⚙️ Can you suggest reasons why cars with fuel cells in are likely to be more successful and popular than battery-powered cars?

1 The diagram below shows a simple electromagnet being used to pick up iron nails.

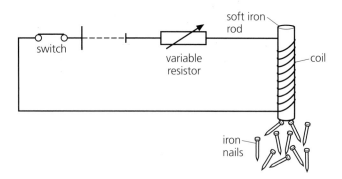

a What happens to the nails if the switch S is opened?

b What would happen to the nails if the soft iron rod was replaced with a rod of steel and the switch then closed and opened. Explain your answer.

c Suggest two ways in which the strength of the electromagnet could be increased.

d Name two situations or pieces of equipment that use an electromagnet.

2 The diagram below shows the electrical circuit for an electric bell.

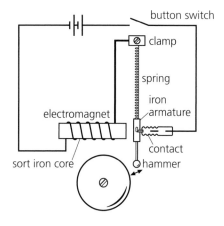

a Explain why the bell would not work if the soft iron core of the electromagnet was replaced by a steel core.

3 The diagram below shows a circuit containing a relay switch. It allows an operator to turn on and off large industrial machinery using a circuit around which a small current flows.

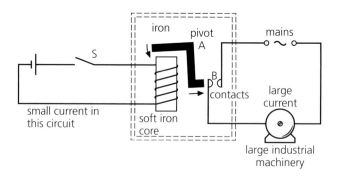

a Explain in detail **i** how the machinery is turned on when switch S is closed **ii** how the machinery is turned off when switch S is opened.

4 The diagram below shows a thick copper wire AB resting on two horizontal copper rods.

a When the switch is closed in which direction will the current flow through the thick copper wire?

b What happens to the thick copper wire when the switch is closed?

c What will happen to the thick copper wire if the magnet is inverted and the switch then closed.

5 The diagram below shows a simple generator. Rotating the loop of wire causes a current which lights the lamp.

a State **three** ways to increase the current produced by the generator.

b This kind of generator produces 'alternating current'. Explain what is meant by the phrase 'alternating current'.

6 The diagram below shows the route followed by domestic electricity in this country.

a Name the device that produces our electrical energy at a power station. Name three fuels which could be used to power this machine. State the principle energy transformation which takes place.

b Suggest one reason why the power lines are suspended high above the ground on pylons.

c What happens to the electricity before it enters our homes? In just one sentence explain how this is done.

d Why is alternating current transmitted rather than direct current?

7 The diagram below shows a transformer being used to change 230 V a.c. to 115 V a.c.

a What kind of transformer is being used in the above circuit?

Key words

The spread numbers in brackets tell you where to find more information.

alternator An a.c. (alternating current) generator. *(7.07)*

circuit breaker An electromagnetic switch that turns off the current in a circuit if this gets too high. It does the same job as a fuse but, unlike a fuse, can be reset. *(7.03)*

electro-magnet A coil wound round a core of iron or Mumetal. It becomes magnetized when a current is passed through the coil, but loses its magnetism when the current is switched off. *(7.03)*

electro-magnetic induction Process in which a voltage is generated in a wire or coil because the magnetic field around it is moving or changing. *(7.06 – 7.07)*

generator A machine that produces a voltage when its shaft is turned. *(7.06, 6.07)*

magnetic field The region around around a magnet where forces act on any magnetic materials that are there. *(7.01)*

magnetic material A material that is attracted to a magnet, and can be magnetized. All magnetic materials contain iron, nickel, or cobalt. *(7.01)*

magnetic poles Points on a magnet where the magnetic forces appear to come from. Each magnet has an N pole and an S pole. *(7.01)*

relay An electromagnetic switch in which a small current in one circuit can be used to switch on or off a much larger current in another. *(7.03)*

transformer A device used to increase or decrease the voltage of an a.c. supply. *(7.07 – 7.08)*

Atoms and nuclei

The aurora borealis, or 'northern lights', as seen from a spacecraft above the Earth. The shimmering curtain of light is produced when atomic particles streaming from the Sun strike atoms and molecules high in the Earth's atmosphere. The Earth's magnetic field concentrates the incoming atomic particles above the north and south polar regions, so that is where aurorae are normally seen.

Inside atoms

Objectives

This spread should help you to
- explain what atoms, elements, and isotopes are
- explain what atomic number and mass number mean

Everything is made of atoms. Atoms are far too small to be seen with any ordinary microscope. However, by shooting tiny atomic particles through them, scientists have been able to develop **models** (descriptions) of their structure. Here is one simple model:

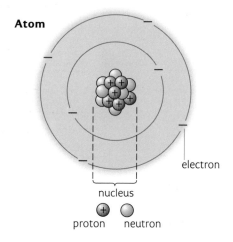

A simple model of the atom. A real nucleus is far too small to be shown to its correct scale. If this atom were the size of a theatre, its nucleus would be smaller than a pea!

- An atom has a central **nucleus** made up of **protons** and **neutrons**. Around this, **electrons** orbit at high speed, at set levels.
- Protons have a positive (+) electric charge. Electrons have an equal negative (–) charge. Normally, an atom has the same number of electrons as protons, so its total charge is zero.
- Protons and neutrons are much heavier than electrons, which add almost nothing to an atom's mass.

Elements and atomic number

All materials are made from about 100 basic substances called **elements**. An atom is the smallest possible 'piece' of an element.

Each element has a different number of protons in its atoms: it has a different **atomic number** (or **proton number**). There are some examples on the left. The atomic number also tells you the number of electrons in the atom.

Element	Chemical symbol	Atomic number (proton number)
hydrogen	H	1
helium	He	2
lithium	Li	3
beryllium	Be	4
boron	B	5
carbon	C	6
nitrogen	N	7
oxygen	O	8
radium	Ra	88
thorium	Th	90
uranium	U	92
plutonium	Pu	94

Isotopes and mass number

The atoms of any one element are not all exactly alike. Some may have more neutrons than others. These different versions of the element are called **isotopes**. Chemically, they behave in exactly the same way, although their atoms have different masses.

Most elements are a mixture of two or more isotopes. You can see some examples in the chart below.

The total number of protons and neutrons in the nucleus is called the **mass number** (or **nucleon number**).

Isotopes have the *same* atomic number but *different* mass numbers. For example:

The metal lithium (atomic number 3) is a mixture of two isotopes with mass numbers 6 and 7. Lithium-7 is the more common: over 93% of lithium atoms are of this type. On the left, you can see how to represent an atom of lithium-7 using a symbol and numbers.

mass number (nucleon number)

$^7_3$Li — symbol for element

atomic number (proton number)

Element	Isotopes				e = electron (−) p = proton (+) n = neutron
hydrogen H	1 e 1 p 0 n hydrogen-1	>99% $^1_1$H	1 e 1 p 1 n hydrogen-2	<1% $^2_1$H	
helium He	2 e 2 p 1 n helium-3	<1% $^3_2$He	2 e 2 p 2 n helium-4	>99% $^4_2$He	
lithium Li	3 e 3 p 3 n lithium-6	7% $^6_3$Li	3 e 3 p 4 n lithium-7	93% $^7_3$Li	

> means 'greater than', < means 'less than'.

Questions

For questions 4 and 5, you will need data from the table of elements on the opposite page.

1 An atom contains *electrons*, *protons*, and *neutrons*.

Which of these particles:

a are outside the nucleus? **b** are uncharged?

c are much lighter than the others?

2 An aluminium atom has an atomic number of 13 and a mass number of 27. How many of the following does it have?

a protons **b** electrons **c** neutrons

3 Chlorine is a mixture of two isotopes, with mass numbers 35 and 37. What is the difference between the two atoms?

4 In symbol form, nitrogen-14 can be written $^{14}_7$N. How can each of the following be written?

a carbon-12 **b** oxygen-16 **c** radium-226

5 Atom X has 6 electrons and a mass number of 12. Atom Y has 6 electrons and a mass number of 14. Atom Z has 8 neutrons and a mass number of 15. Identify the elements X, Y, and Z.

Nuclear radiation

Some materials contain atoms with unstable nuclei. In time, each nucleus breaks up, or rearranges itself. As it does so, it shoots out a tiny particle, a burst of wave energy, or both. The particles and waves 'radiate' from the nucleus, so they are called **nuclear radiation**. The materials they come from are **radioactive**.

Elements are a mixture of isotopes. In a 'radioactive material', it is really particular isotopes that are radioactive. The chart below gives some examples. Radioactive isotopes are called **radioisotopes**.

Isotopes		
stable nuclei	*unstable nuclei, radioactive*	*found in*
carbon-12 carbon-13	carbon-14	air, plants, animals
potassium-39 potassium-41	potassium-40	rocks, plants, sea water
	uranium-234 uranium-235 uranium-238	rocks

Questions

1 Name one radioisotope which occurs naturally in living things.

2 What are the three main types of nuclear radiation?

Alpha, beta, and gamma radiation

There are three main types of nuclear radiation: **alpha particles**, **beta particles**, and **gamma rays**. The chart on the opposite page gives their main properties (features). Gamma rays are the most penetrating and alpha particles the least, as shown below:

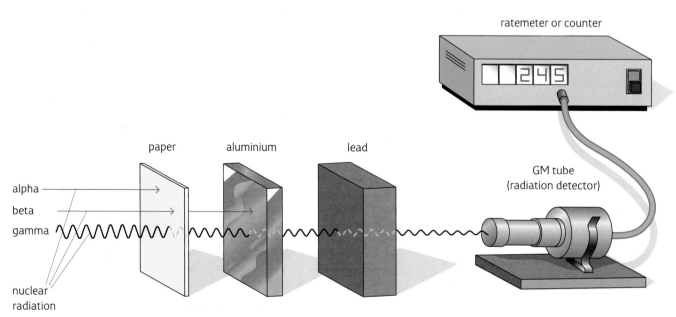

Alpha, beta, and gamma radiation can be detected using a **Geiger–Müller tube** (**GM tube** for short). The GM tube can be connected to the following:

- **A ratemeter** This gives a reading in counts per second. For example, if 50 alpha particles are detected by a GM tube every second, the ratemeter reads 50 counts per second.
- **An electronic counter** This counts the *total* number of particles (or bursts of gamma radiation) detected by the tube.
- **An amplifier and loudspeaker** The loudspeaker 'clicks' when each particle or burst of gamma radiation is detected.

Ionizing radiation

Nuclear radiation can strip electrons from atoms in its path. As a result, the atoms are left electrically charged. Charged atoms are called **ions**, so nuclear radiation causes **ionization**. Ultraviolet and X-rays also cause ionization. Living cells are very sensitive to ionization. It can completely upset their life processes.

Here, a GM tube is being used to check for traces of radioactive dust on the ground.

Nuclear radiation	Alpha particles	Beta particles	Gamma rays
	each particle is 2 protons + 2 neutrons	each particle is an electron (formed when the nucleus breaks up)	electromagnetic waves similar to X-rays
Electric charge	positive	negative	no charge
Ionizing effect	strong	weak	very weak
Penetrating effect	not very penetrating, stopped by thick sheet of paper, or skin	penetrating, but stopped by thick sheet of aluminium	highly penetrating, never completely stopped, though lead and very thick concrete reduce strength

Questions

3 What is a GM tube used for?

4 Nuclear radiation causes *ionization*. What does this mean?

5 *alpha   beta   gamma*

Which of these three types of radiation:

a is a form of electromagnetic radiation?

b carries positive charge?

c carries negative charge?

d can penetrate a thick sheet of lead?

e is stopped by skin or thick paper?

f is similar to X-rays?

g is the most ionizing?

Exposed to radiation

Objectives

This spread should help you to

- explain why radioactive materials are dangerous
- describe what background radiation is, and where it comes from

Nuclear power stations produce radioactive waste. The containers that carry the waste must be strong enough to withstand crashes like the one above. If any leaked out, it would be a health hazard.

Radiation dangers

Because of its ionizing effect, nuclear radiation can damage or destroy living cells. It can stop vital organs in the body working properly, and cause cancer. The stronger the radiation, the greater the risk.

Dangers from inside the body Radioactive gas and dust are especially dangerous because they can be taken into the body with air, food, or drink. Once absorbed, they are difficult to remove, and their radiation can cause damage in cells deep in the body. Alpha radiation is the most harmful because it is the most highly ionizing.

Dangers from outside the body Normally, there is less risk from radioactive sources *outside* the body. Sources in nuclear power stations and laboratories are well shielded, and their radiation gets weaker as you move further away from them. Beta and gamma rays are the most dangerous because they can penetrate to internal organs. But alpha particles are stopped by the skin.

This film badge detects the total amount of radiation the wearer has been exposed to.

Workers in nuclear power stations have to wear a film badge like the one on the left. It reacts to nuclear radiation rather like the film in a camera reacts to light. Every month, the film is developed, to check that its wearer hasn't been exposed to too much radiation.

Background radiation

We are exposed to a small amount of radiation all the time because of radioactive material in our surroundings. This is called **background radiation**. It mainly comes from natural sources such as soil, rocks, air, building materials, food and drink – and even space.

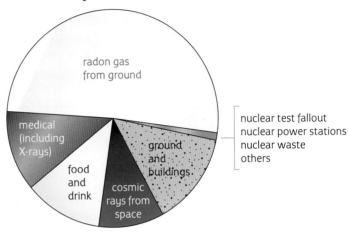

Where background radiation comes from. (These proportions are averages. The actual proportions vary from one area to another).

In some areas, over half of the background radiation comes from radioactive radon gas (radon-222) seeping out of rocks – especially some types of granite. In high-risk areas, houses may need extra ventilation to stop the gas collecting. Sometimes, a sealed floor is used to stop the gas entering in the first place.

When the radiation from a radioactive source is measured, the reading always *includes* any background radiation. To find the reading for the source alone, you must measure the background radiation and take that reading away from the total.

Questions

1 What is the biggest source of background radiation?

2 Radon gas seeps out of rocks underground. Why is it important to stop radon collecting in houses?

3 **a** Which is the most dangerous type of radiation from radioactive materials absorbed by the body?

b Why is this radiation less dangerous outside the body?

4 In the experiment on the right:

a What is the count rate due to background radiation?

b What is the count rate due to the source alone?

c If the source emits one type of radiation only, what type is it? (You may need information from the previous spread to answer this.)

count rate (average)...	counts per second
...with the source in place	28
...with the source and block in place	18
...with the source and block removed	2

Radioactive decay

The break-up of unstable nuclei is called **radioactive decay**. It happens completely at random, and isn't affected by pressure, temperature, or chemical change. You can't tell which nucleus is going to break up next, or when. However, some types of nucleus are more unstable than others and decay at a faster rate.

Activity

In a radioactive sample, the average number of nuclei breaking up per second is called the **activity**. Activity is measured in **becquerels** (Bq). For example:

Iodine-131 is a radioactive isotope of iodine. It decays by shooting out beta particles. If, in a sample of iodine-131, 40 nuclei are breaking up every second, then 40 beta particles are being shot out every second, and the activity of the sample is 40 Bq.

Half-life

Time in days	Activity in Bq
0	40
8	20
16	10
24	5

*Every 8 days, the activity halves. Iodine-131 has a **half-life** of 8 days.*

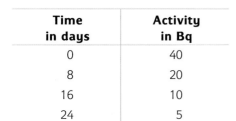

The table and graph above show how the average activity of a sample of iodine-131 varies with time. To begin with, 40 nuclei are breaking up every second, so the activity is 40 Bq. But as time goes on, there are fewer and fewer unstable nuclei left to decay, so the activity gets less and less. After 8 days, the activity has fallen to half its original value. After another 8 days, the activity has halved again... and so on. Iodine-131 has a **half-life** of 8 days.

With experimental results, the points on the graph are irregular (they jump about) because radioactive decay is a random process. The curve above is really a 'line of best fit', as shown on the left.

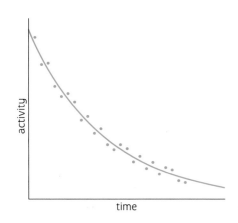

The curve is really a 'line of best fit' between irregular points.

Radioactive isotope	Half-life
boron-12	0.02 seconds
radon-220	52 seconds
iodine-128	25 minutes
radon-222	3.8 days
strontium-90	28 years
radium-226	1602 years
carbon-14	5730 years
plutonium-239	24 400 years
uranium-235	710 million years
uranium-238	4500 million years

To get a graph like the one on the opposite page, a Geiger–Müller (GM) tube is used to detect the radiation from the sample. The number of counts per second is proportional to the activity – but not equal to it, because not all the beta particles from the sample go into the detector.

The half-lives of some other radioactive isotopes are given in the table on the left.

> The half-life of a radioactive isotope is the time taken for the activity of any sample to fall to half its original value.

New atoms from old

When an atom shoots out an alpha or beta particle, the number of protons in its nucleus changes, so it becomes an atom of a completely different element. Here is an example:

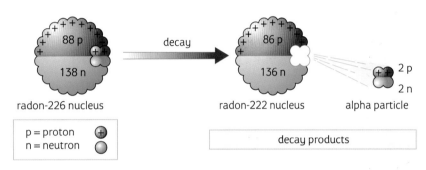

radon-226 nucleus   radon-222 nucleus   alpha particle

p = proton   ⊕
n = neutron   ◯

decay products

Did you know?

Isotopes

Most elements are a mixture of isotopes – different versions of the element, with the same number of protons in the nucleus of each atom, but different numbers of neutrons.

Above, a nucleus of radium-226 decays by shooting out an alpha particle. As a result, the nucleus loses 2 protons and 2 neutrons, so it changes into a nucleus of radon-222. This too is radioactive.

Radon-222 and the alpha particle are the **decay products**.

Questions

To answer questions 1 and 2, you will need information from the table of half-lives.

1. If samples of strontium-90 and radium-226 both have the same activity today, which will have the lower activity in 10 years' time?

2. If the activity of a sample of iodine-128 is 800 Bq, what would you expect the activity to be after:

   a 25 minutes? **b** 50 minutes? **c** 100 minutes?

3. The graph on the right shows how the activity of a small radioactive sample varied with time.

   a Why are the points not on a smooth curve?

   b Estimate the half-life of the sample.

Using radioactivity

Some radioisotopes exist naturally; others must be produced artificially in a nuclear reactor. Here are some of their uses.

Using tracers

Radioisotopes can be detected in very small (and safe) quantities, so they can be used as **tracers** – their movements can be tracked. Here are two examples:

- Checking whether a patient's thyroid gland is taking in iodine properly. The patient drinks a liquid containing iodine-123, a gamma emitter. A detector measures the activity of the tracer to find out how quickly iodine becomes concentrated in the gland.
- Detecting leaks in underground pipes by adding a tracer to the fluid in the pipe.

For tests like these, artificial radioisotopes with short half-lives are used so that there is almost no radioactivity left after a few days.

Radiotherapy

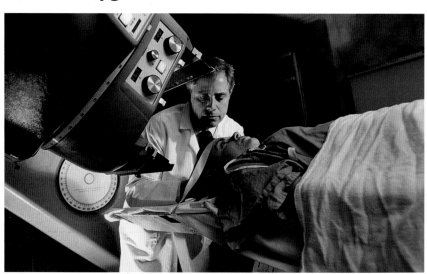

A concentrated beam of gamma rays is pointed at one small area of this patient's body to kill the cancer cells in a tumour.

Gamma rays can penetrate deep into the body and kill living cells. So a highly concentrated beam from a cobalt-60 source can be used to kill cancer cells. Treatment like this is called **radiotherapy**.

Testing for cracks

Gamma rays are like X-rays, so they can be used to photograph metals to reveal cracks. A cobalt-60 gamma source is compact and does not need an electrical power source like an X-ray tube.

Objectives

This spread should help you to

- describe some of the uses of radioisotopes

Did you know?

Nuclear essentials

Elements exist in different versions, called isotopes. Some are radioactive: they are **radioisotopes**. Of the radiation they give off, gamma rays are very penetrating, beta particles less so, and alpha particles least of all. All three types of radiation damage or destroy living cells if absorbed.

Questions

1. **a** What are *radioisotopes*?
   b Where are artificial radioisotopes produced?
   c Give *two* medical uses of radioisotopes.
2. Give *two* uses of gamma radiation.

Thickness monitoring

Some material manufacturing processes need to produce a steady thickness. The diagram shows one way of doing this. The thickness of tyre cord is being adjusted:

The moving band of tyre cord has a beta source on one side and a detector on the other. If the cord from the rollers becomes too thin, more beta radiation reaches the detector. This sends signals to the control unit, which adjusts the gap between the rollers.

Dating materials

As time goes on, any radioactivity in a material slowly dies away. This idea can be used to estimate its age. For example:

There is carbon in the atmosphere (in carbon dioxide) and in the bodies of living things. A small amount is radioactive carbon-14, which is continually being formed in the upper atmosphere. While plants and animals are alive, they absorb and give out carbon as they feed and breathe, so the proportion of carbon-14 in their bodies stays the same. But when they die, no more carbon is taken in and the proportion of carbon-14 reduces because of radioactive decay.

By measuring the activity of a sample, the age of the remains can be estimated. This is called **carbon dating**. It can be used to find the age of organic materials such as wood and cloth.

The age of some rocks can also be estimated by measuring the proportions of different isotopes in them.

Human remains from a Danish peat bog. Carbon dating showed that this man died around 220–240 BC.

Questions

3 In the thickness monitoring system shown above:

  a why is a beta source used, rather than an alpha or gamma source?

  b what is the effect on the detector if the thickness of the tyre cord increases?

4 Doctors and scientists sometimes use radioactive tracers.

  a What is a radioactive tracer?

  b Describe one use of a radioactive tracer.

  c Why is it important to use radioactive tracers with short half-lives?

5 Carbon-14 is a rare, radioactive isotope of carbon. Explain why scientists might be interested in measuring the amount of carbon-14 in the remains of an ancient plant or animal, or piece of wood or cloth.

Fission power

Like most power stations, the nuclear power station on the right uses heat to make steam for the turbines which turn its generators. But the heat doesn't come from burning coal, oil, or gas. It comes from the nuclei of uranium atoms as they break up in a **nuclear reactor**. One tonne of nuclear fuel can deliver as much energy as 55 tonnes of coal.

In nuclear fuel, the 'magic ingredient' is a rare type of uranium called uranium-235. If a nucleus of uranium-235 is hit by a stray neutron, it splits, releasing energy and more neutrons. These may go on to split other nuclei...and so on, in a **chain reaction**. The splitting process is called **nuclear fission**.

In a reactor, pellets of nuclear fuel are in sealed cans in the reactor's core. As most neutrons tend to escape before hitting anything else, the core must carefully designed to make sure that the chain reaction keeps going. The reaction can be slowed down by lowering control rods to absorb neutrons.

In the reactor below, the heat from fission is carried to a boiler by water which circulates through the core.

A pressurized-water reactor (PWR).

Nuclear waste

When cans of nuclear fuel are 'spent' (exhausted), they must be removed from the reactor's core and replaced. They contain highly radioactive materials, including plutonium-239. Plutonium is used in nuclear weapons. It is also highly toxic. Breathed in as dust, the smallest amount can kill.

A cooling pond at a reprocessing plant.

Spent fuel cans are taken to a reprocessing plant where unused fuel and plutonium are removed. The remaining waste is sealed off and stored with thick shielding around it.

Radioactive waste is extremely dangerous. Some isotopes have long half-lives and stay radioactive for thousands of years. No one really knows how to store them safely for such a long time. If they are buried, geologists must be sure that the rocks are stable and won't crack or move over that period.

Fusion future?

The Sun is powered by **nuclear fusion**: energy is released when nuclei of hydrogen 'fuse' (join) together to form helium. For fusion to occur, hydrogen must be kept compressed at a very high temperature: for example 15 million °C in the Sun's core.

On Earth, no ordinary container can hold hydrogen at such a high temperature and keep it compressed. But the one above is no ordinary container. Scientists have developed it for fusion experiments. It uses a magnetic field to trap the super-hot hydrogen.

Practical fusion reactors are many years away. But they could bring huge benefits. Their fuel, hydrogen, is plentiful and can be extracted from sea water. Their main waste material, helium, isn't radioactive. And they have built-in safety: if the reactor fails, fusion stops.

Talking points

⚠ Can you describe ways in which a nuclear power station is similar to a fuel-burning power station?

⚠ Can you describe ways in which a nuclear power station is different from a fuel-burning power station?

⚠ Why are 'spent' nuclear fuel cans such a problem?

⚠ When fusion reactors are developed, what advantages are they likely to have over today's nuclear reactors?

1 There are two types of electric charge, positive (+) and negative (−). Both types are found in the atom.

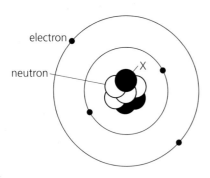

a What type of charge does an electron have?

b What is particle X called?

c What type of charge does particle X have?

d How many particles of type X would you expect the atom above to have? Explain your answer. (Note: the diagram does not show all the particles of type X.)

e When a current flows through a wire, it is some of the particles from the atoms which are moving along. Which particles?

2 a The diagram below represents an atom of nitrogen-14 ($^{14}_{7}$N).

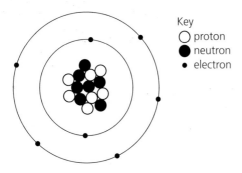

Complete this table of data for nitrogen-14.

Particle	Number in atom	Charge
proton		
neutron		
electron		

b The element chlorine has two 'isotopes'. What are isotopes?

c Draw diagrams of the two isotopes chlorine-35 ($^{35}_{17}$Cl) and chlorine-37 ($^{37}_{17}$Cl).

3 A radioactive source is emitting all three types of radiation α, β and γ.

a What is an α particle?

b What is a β particle?

c What is a γ ray?

d From where are these radioactive particles and rays being emitted?

e Name one piece of apparatus that could be used to detect radiation.

f Name one material through which β particles and rays can pass but not α particles.

g Name one material through which only very energetic γ rays can pass.

4 A piece of rock is placed in front of a radiation detector. The count rate is high. A piece of paper is wrapped around the rock and the count rate drops to half its original value. A piece of silver foil is now wrapped around the rock and the count rate drops to zero.

a Which type(s) of radiation is/are being emitted by the rock? Explain your answer.

b Why are radioactive materials often stored in lead lined containers?

5 Two students are carrying out an experiment to discover how much β radiation passes through different thicknesses of aluminium.

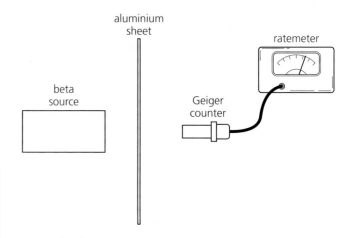

At the beginning of the experiment they measured the background radiation. It was 100 counts per minute.

a Suggest two possible sources of the background radiation.

The students then recorded the count rates for the different thicknesses of aluminium. Their results are shown in the table below.

thickness of aluminium in mm	1.0	2.0	3.0	4.0	5.0	6.0	7.0	8.0	9.0
actual count rate in counts per min	1120	620	300	240	180	150	120	100	100
corrected count rate in counts per min	1020								

b Finish the table by filling in the seven missing corrected count rates.

c Plot a graph of the results (count rate – *y* axis, thickness of aluminium – *x* axis).

d Which result does not fit the pattern?

e What is the minimum thickness of aluminium needed to stop β particles from the source reaching the Geiger counter?

6 In a papermaking plant, a radioactive source and detector can be used for testing the thickness of the paper as it is rolled out.

The radioactive source in the diagram above gives out beta particles.

a What are β particles?

b What device could be used as a detector?

c If the paper is thicker than normal, what effect will this have on the reading on the detector?

d Why should the radioactive source be a β source, rather than one that gives out α particles or γ rays?

e Some people could be worried that the radiation might 'make the paper radioactive'. What answer would you give them?

7 The diagram below shows a lady trying to detect a leak in an oil pipe below the ground. A radioactive isotope has been added to the oil in the pipe.

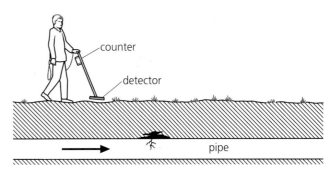

a Describe what happens when the detector passes over the leak. Explain your answer.

b What kind of radiation should the radioactive isotope be emitting? Explain your answer.

8 The graph below shows how the radiation emitted per minute by a sample of uranium-238 ($^{238}_{92}U$) changes with time.

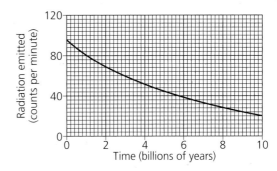

a After how many years has the count rate dropped to 80 counts per minute?

b After how many years has the count rate dropped to 40 counts per minute?

c What is the half-life of uranium-238?

9 In some parts of Britain high levels of background radiation are caused by radon gas. The element radium-224 ($^{224}_{88}Ra$) decays to form radon-220 ($^{220}_{86}Rn$).

a From where within a radium atom is the particle emitted?

Radium-224 has a 'half life' of 3.6 days.

b What is meant by the phrase 'half life'?

c If the initial count rate of a sample of radium-224 is 800 counts per sec what is the count rate of this sample after **i** 3.6 days **ii** 10.8 days?

Key words

The spread numbers in brackets tell you where to find more information.

activity   The average number of unstable nuclei decaying (breaking up) per second in a radioactive material. If 100 nuclei are decaying per second, the activity is 100 becquerels (Bq). *(8.04)*

alpha particles   Positively (+) charged particles given off by some radioactive materials. Each alpha particle is made up of two protons and two neutrons. *(8.02)*

atomic number   The number of protons in an atom. Sometimes called the proton number. *(8.01)*

background radiation   The low level of radiation that is always present, mainly because of radioactive materials in the ground and air. *(8.03)*

beta particles   Negatively (–) charged particles given off by some radioactive materials. Each beta particle is an electron. *(8.02)*

electron   Negatively (–) charged particle that moves around the nucleus of an atom. *(8.01, 2.01)*

gamma rays   Electromagnetic waves given off by some radioactive materials. They are similar to X-rays. *(8.02)*

Geiger–Müller tube (G–M tube)   Device used for detecting radiation from radioactive materials. *(8.02)*

half-life   The time taken for the activity of a radioactive sample to halve. Also the time taken for half the unstable nuclei present to decay (break up). *(8.04)*

isotopes   Different versions of an element. Isotopes have the same number of protons (and electrons) in their atoms, but a different number of neutrons. *(8.01)*

mass number   The total number of protons and neutrons in an atom. Sometimes called the nucleon number. *(8.01)*

neutron   Uncharged particle in the nucleus of an atom. *(8.01)*

nucleus   The centre of an atom, made up (in most cases) of protons and neutrons. *(8.01)*

proton   Positively (+) charged particle in the nucleus of an atom. *(8.01)*

radiation (nuclear)   Particles or waves shot out from the unstable nuclei of atoms in radioactive materials. The main types are alpha particles, beta particles, and gamma rays. *(8.02)*

radioactive decay   The break-up of unstable nuclei in the atoms of a radiuoactive material. *(8.04)*

radioactive material   A material that gives off nuclear radiation – usually alpha, beta, or gamma rays. *(8.02)*

Exam-style questions

1 A car driver drives from his home at a slow, steady speed. On reaching the motorway he accelerates rapidly and then travels at a high constant speed. Leaving the motorway he decelerates and comes to a halt at a junction.

   a Sketch a speed-time graph for the driver's journey.

   b Sketch a distance-time graph for the driver's journey.

   c Calculate the driver's average speed in km/h if he travels 40 km in 30 min.

2 The diagram below shows a velocity-time graph for a free-fall parachutist.

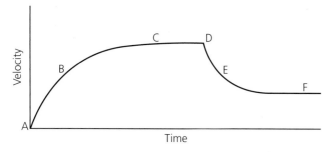

Assuming the acceleration due to gravity is 10 m/s²

   a Why is the acceleration of the parachutist decreasing in part B of the graph?

   b Explain why the parachutist is travelling at his terminal velocity in part C of the graph.

   c What has happened at point D on the graph?

   d What is happening to the parachutist in part E of the graph?

   e What is happening to the parachutist in part F of the graph?

3 An electric motor is a device for changing electrical energy into kinetic energy. Suggest a device which will carry out the following energy changes:

   a electrical energy to heat and light energy

   b chemical energy to electrical energy

   c light energy to electrical energy

   d sound energy to electrical energy

   e electrical energy to sound

   f chemical energy to heat and light.

4 a Explain the following sentences.

     Coal is a non-renewable source of energy.

     Wind is a renewable source of energy.

   b Name one other non-renewable source of energy.

   c Name one other renewable source of energy.

d Give one advantage and one disadvantage of using the source of energy you have given as an answer for part c.

5 The diagram below shows a simple series circuit containing a cell, a switch and a bulb. When the switch is closed a current of 0.2A flows through the bulb.

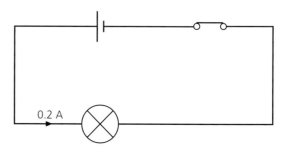

   a What current will flow from the cell if the second bulb is now connected in parallel with the first bulb?

6 The diagram below shows a battery, ammeter and bulb connected in series. A voltmeter is connected in parallel with the bulb.

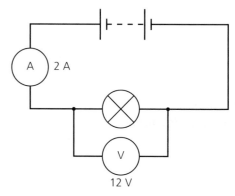

   a Calculate the power of the bulb.

   b How much energy is converted by the bulb in 10 s?

   c What energy change takes place inside the bulb?

7 There are three commonly available fuses that can be used in a three-pin mains plug. These are rated at 3 A, 5 A and 13 A.

Which of these three fuses would be suitable for use with each of the following appliances? Electricity from the mains is supplied at 230 V.

   a A bulb rated at 60 W.

   b A TV set rated at 600 W

   c A hair drier rated at 1.1 kW.

   d A kettle rated at 2 kW.

e Explain what happens to a fuse if too much current passes through the circuit.

8 The diagram below shows the inside of a three-pin plug.

a What is the name of pin A?

b What is the name of pin B?

c What is the colour of the wire connected to the Earth pin?

d Explain why there is an Earth pin.

e What is D?

9 a If electrical energy costs 7p per kW h calculate the cost of the following:

   i a 3 kW fire turned on for 6 hours

   ii a 1.2 kW hair drier for 30 mins

   iii a 100 W bulb for 10 hours.

b What is the National Grid?

10 The diagram below shows two resistors connected in parallel.

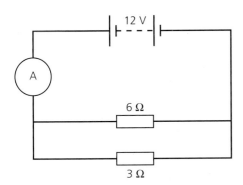

a What is A?

b Calculate the current flowing through the 6 Ω resistor.

c Calculate the current flowing through the 3 Ω resistor.

d What current flows through A?

11 A student using the circuit shown below investigates the relationship between the current flowing through a resistor and the p.d. (voltage) across it.

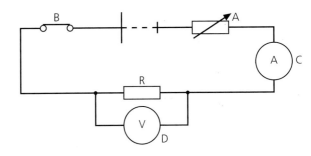

a What is A?

b What is B?

c What is C?

d What is D?

The student's results are shown in the table below.

p.d./V	0	2	4	6	8	10	12
current/A	0	0.25	0.50	0.80	1.00	1.25	1.50

e Plot a graph of p.d. against current.

f Which result appears to have been measured incorrectly?

g What is the resistance of the resistor R?

12 A car headlamp is rated at 12 V 36 W.

a What energy change takes place inside the bulb?

b How rapidly does this energy change take place?

c Calculate the current which flows through the bulb.

d Calculate the resistance of the bulb.

13 The graph below shows part of the journey of a bus driver. After travelling along the main road for several minutes he pulls into the bus station. Sometime later he drives out of the bus station and continues his journey.

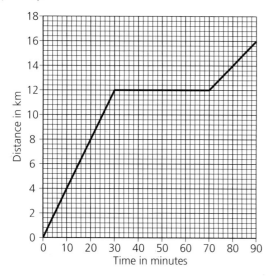

a How far did the bus driver travel before pulling into the bus station?

b How long did the bus driver stop in the bus station?

c What was the average speed of the bus before pulling into the bus station?

d Was the journey after the stop at a faster or slower speed? Explain your answer.

14 The diagram below shows a spanner being used to undo a nut on a car wheel.

a Calculate the moment created by the force trying to undo the nut.

b Suggest how you could increase the moment applied to the nut without increasing the applied force.

15 The diagram below shows waves being produced in a ripple tank by a wave machine.

a How many water waves are shown in the diagram?

b If the above waves were produced in 2.5 s what is their frequency?

c If the wavelength of the water waves is 5 cm calculate their speed.

16 A crane lifts a load of 500 N through a height of 30m in 20 s.

a What kind of energy has the load gained after the lift has been completed?

b Calculate the work done by the crane.

c Suggest one reason why the crane will have done more work than the value you calculated in part **b**.

d Calculate the power of the crane.

17 The table below shows the results obtained by a pupil when he applied different loads to a spring and then measured its length.

Load/N	25	50	75	100	125	150
Length of spring/cm	8.0	9.0	10.0	11.0	12.0	13.0

a Draw a graph of load (*y* axis) against length of spring (*x* axis).

b What was the length of the spring when it was unstretched?

c What was the length of the spring when the load was 60 N?

d What load was needed to stretch the spring to a length of 14.0 cm?

e What load was needed to produce an extension of 4.0 cm?

18 The diagram below shows an electrical circuit.

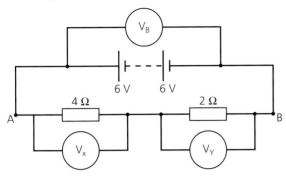

a What is the voltage of the battery V_B?

b What is the total resistance between points A and B?

c What is the current flowing through the circuit?

d What is the voltage (V_X) across the 4 Ω resistor?

e What is the voltage (V_Y) across the 2 Ω resistor?

19 The diagram below shows a bar magnet, and a coil of wire connected to a sensitive ammeter.

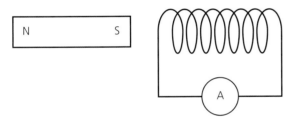

As the magnet was pushed slowly into the coil the ammeter pointer moved 10 divisions to the right.

What would you expect to happen

a If the magnet is pulled slowly out of the coil?

b The magnet is held stationary inside the coil?

c The magnet is turned around so that its north pole is nearer the coil. The magnet is then pushed quickly into the coil?

d Explain in your own words why the ammeter deflects.

20 The diagram below shows the flow of heat from the inside of a house to the outside through a cavity wall.

a Why will heat flow from the inside of a house to the outside?

b By what method is heat transferred through the bricks?

c By what method is heat transferred across the air gap?

d Suggest what could be done to reduce the rate at which heat flows across the air gap.

21 Coal, oil and gas are fossil fuels.

a How is the energy contained in these fuels released?

b Explain briefly how fossil fuels are formed.

c Why are fossil fuels called non-renewable sources of energy?

d Name one renewable fuel.

e Explain how the use of fossil fuels might lead to 'global warming'.

22 The diagram below shows the flow of energy through a coal-burning power station.

$$\text{efficiency} = \frac{\text{useful energy output}}{\text{total energy input}} \times 100\%$$

a Calculate the efficiency of the above power station.

b Explain how the energy released when the coal is burned is used to produce electricity.

c How is this electrical energy then sent to towns and cities many miles from the power station?

23 The diagram below shows how light travels along an optical fibre.

a Explain why the ray of light does not emerge from the sides of the optical fibre.

b Describe one use of an optical fibre.

24 The graph below shows how a spring stretches when a force is applied to it.

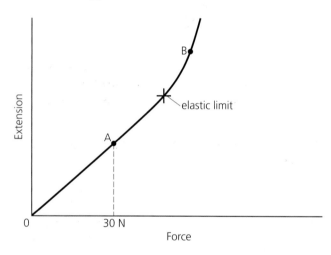

a Describe what would happen to the spring if forces were applied to it until it reached point A on the graph and then the forces were removed?

b Describe what would happen if the spring was stretched to point B on the graph and then the forces removed.

c If a force of 10 N caused the spring to stretch by 5 cm what would be the extension of the string if 20 N was applied to it?

25 The diagram below shows the northern part of the Earth.

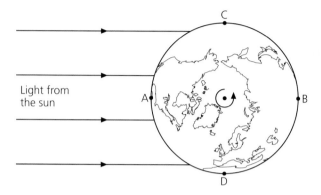

Approximately what time of day is it

a at point A

b at point B

c at point C

d at point D on the Earth's surface.

e How long does it take the Earth to make one complete rotation around its axis?

26 These objects are all part of the Universe.

planet moon satellite constellation Sun comet galaxy

a Which object is a very large collection of stars?

b Which two objects orbit the Sun?

c Which two objects could orbit a planet?

d Which object is a small collection of stars?

e Which is the largest object in our solar system?

27 The diagram below shows what happens to the radiation from three different radioactive substances when different materials are put in front of them.

a Which type of radiation is being emitted by each of the three sources?

b Which of these three types of radiation are charged?

c Which of these three types of radiation is the strongest ionizer?

d Name one way in which all three types of radiation could be detected.

28 The diagram below shows a toy car.

a Name three energy sources which could be placed in the car to make it move.

b What kind of energy does the car have when it is moving?

c Explain as fully as you can the phrase 'renewable source of energy'.

29 The diagram below shows a tumble dryer.

a Copy out the sentence below and fill in the missing words.

The tumble dryer converts _____ energy into _____ energy and _____ energy.

b The power of the dryer is 1.5kW.

Calculate the number of units of electricity it uses if it is turned on for 40 minutes.

c Calculate the cost of using the dryer for this time if the cost of 1 unit of electricity is 9p.

30 This question is about the electromagnetic spectrum.

a Which statement about electromagnetic waves is correct?

A They all have the same wavelength.

B They all have the same frequency.

C They all travel at the same speed in air.

b Name TWO types of electromagnetic wave which could be used to cook food.

c Name ONE type of electromagnetic wave used for communicating over large distances.

d Name ONE type of electromagnetic wave we use to see

e Describe the danger of ultraviolet radiation to our health.

f Suggest TWO ways in which people can reduce the health risk from ultraviolet radiation.

g Name ONE source of γ rays.

31 The diagram below shows a sledge sliding across some ice.

a As sledges slide across the ice, they slow down and eventually stop. Explain why this happens.

b Write down **two** effects the sliding sledges will have on the ice.

32 Prisms can be used to alter the direction of a ray of light.

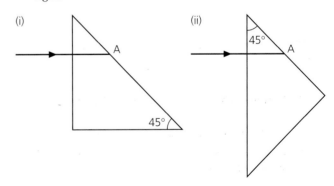

a Copy the diagrams below into your book and complete them showing accurately the paths the rays will take.

b What happens to each of the rays at point A inside the prisms?

c By how many degrees does each prism alter the directions of the rays of light?

d Name one use of a reflecting prism.

How to revise

There is no one method of revising that works for everyone. It is therefore important to discover the approach that suits you best. These guidelines may help you.

Give yourself plenty of time There are very few people who can revise everything 'the night before' and still do well in an examination the next day. You need to plan your revision to begin several weeks before the examinations start.

Plan your revision timetable Draw up a revision timetable well before the examinations start. Once you have done this, follow it – don't be sidetracked. Stick your timetable somewhere prominent where you will keep seeing it – or better still put several around your home!

Relax You will be working very hard revising. It is as important to give yourself some free time to relax as it is to work. So build some leisure time into your revision timetable.

Ask others Friends, relatives, and teachers will be happy to help if you ask them. Don't just give up on something that is causing you a problem. And don't forget your parents too!

Find a quiet corner Find the conditions in which you can revise most efficiently. Many people think they can revise in a noisy, busy atmosphere – most cannot! And don't try to revise in front of the television. Revision in a distracting environment is very inefficient.

Use routemaps or checklists Use routemaps, checklists, or other listing devices to help you work your way logically through the material. When you have completed a topic, tick it off. Tick off topics you already feel confident about. That way you won't waste time revising unnecessarily.

Make short notes and use colours As you read through your work or your textbooks, make brief notes of the key ideas and facts as you go along. But be sure to concentrate on understanding the ideas rather than just memorizing the facts. Use colours and highlighters to help you.

Practise answering questions As you finish revising each topic, try answering some questions. At first you may need to refer to your notes or textbooks. As you gain confidence you will be able to attempt questions unaided, just as you will in the exam.

Give yourself a break When you are revising, work for perhaps an hour, then reward yourself with a short break of 10 to 15 minutes while you do something different. Look out the window, stretch your legs, have a soft or hot drink. But when your 10 or 15 minutes are up, get back to work!

Success in examinations

Most people become a bit nervous about an important examination. If you have done most of your work consistently for two years and revised effectively, the following steps should help you to minimize anxiety and ensure that your examination results reflect all your hard work.

Be prepared Make sure you have everything you need ready the night before, including pens, pencils, ruler, and calculator. Check that you have anything else required well in advance.

Read carefully Before you start, spend a few minutes reading the paper all the way through. Make sure you know exactly what you have to do.

Plan your time Work out how much time you should spend on each question, based on how many marks it has. Allow yourself a few minutes at the end of the exam to check through your work.

Answer the question! When you are ready to start a question, read through it again carefully to make sure it really does say what you think it says. Follow the instructions to the letter: you will get marks for answering the question but not for giving other information about the subject.

Present your work clearly Write as clearly as you possibly can in the time available and think through what you are going to write before you begin writing. Draw diagrams clearly and simply, using single lines where appropriate. Label your diagrams and make sure the label lines point exactly to the relevant places. The examiner will be trying to award you marks – make it as easy for him or her to do so!

Keep calm!!! If you find a question you have no idea about, don't panic! Breathe slowly and deeply and have another look. It's likely that if you stay calm and think clearly, the question will start to make more sense, or at least you may be able to answer part of it. If not, then don't agonize about it – concentrate first on the questions you can answer.

$$speed \ (m/s) = \frac{distance \ moved \ (m)}{time \ taken \ (s)}$$

velocity (m/s) is speed in a particular direction

$$acceleration \ (m/s^2) = \frac{change \ in \ velocity \ (m/s)}{time \ taken \ (s)}$$

weight (N) = mass (kg) × gravitational field
                                                    strength

(gravitational field strength = g = 10 N/m^2
near Earth's surface)

work done (J) = force (N) × distance moved (m)
                                    in direction of force

work done (J) = energy transformed (J)

(energy transformed can also be called energy
transferred)

gain in gravitational potential energy (J)
                = weight (N) × gain in height (m)
                = mass (kg) × g × gain in height (m)

kinetic energy = $\frac{1}{2}$ × mass × speed^2
        (J)   (kg)   (m/s)

$$power \ (W) = \frac{energy \ transformed \ (J)}{time \ taken \ (s)}$$

$$= \frac{work \ done \ (J)}{time \ taken \ (s)}$$

$$efficiency = \frac{useful \ energy \ output \ (J)}{energy \ input (J)}$$

$$= \frac{useful \ work \ done \ (J)}{energy \ input \ (J)}$$

$$= \frac{useful \ power \ ouput \ (W)}{power \ input \ (W)}$$

energy transformed = power × time
        (J)   (W)   (s)

energy transformed = power × time
        (kW h)   (kW)   (hours)

For waves:
speed (m/s) = frequency (Hz) × wavelength (m)

$$resistance \ (\Omega) = \frac{voltage \ (V)}{current \ (A)}$$

power (W) = voltage (V) × current (A)

$$density \ (kg/m^3) = \frac{mass \ (kg)}{volume \ (m^3)}$$

$$pressure \ (Pa) = \frac{force \ (N)}{area \ m^2}$$

moment of a force (N m)
        = force (N) × perpendicular distance from
                                    pivot (m)

Units and symbols

Units and symbols

Quantity	Unit	Symbol
mass	kilogram	kg
length	metre	m
time	second	s
force	newton	N
weight	newton	N
pressure	pascal	Pa
energy	joule	J
work	joule	J
power	watt	W
voltage	volt	V
current	ampere	A
resistance	ohm	Ω
charge	coulomb	C
temperature	kelvin	K
temperature	degree Celsius	°C

Bigger and smaller

To make units bigger or smaller, prefixes are put in front of them:

micro (μ)	=	1 millionth	=	0.000001
milli (m)	=	1 thousandth	=	0.001
kilo (k)	=	1 thousand	=	1000
mega (M)	=	1 million	=	1000000

For example

1 micrometre	= 1 μm	= 0.000001 m
1 millisecond	= 1 ms	= 0.001 s
1 kilometre	= 1 km	= 1000 m
1 megatonne	= 1 Mt	= 1000000 t

wires joining	wires crossing	lamp/bulb — ⊗ or	ammeter (A)
voltmeter (V)	switch — or	cell (+ terminal)	battery (several cells)
d.c. power supply (+ −)	a.c. power supply	resistor	variable resistors
thermistor	light-dependent resistor (LDR)	heater	fuse · transformer
diode	light-emitting diode (LED)	earth	relay · buzzer

Note: The answers are arranged in three sections

    End of spread questions
    End of chapter questions
    Exam-style questions

End of spread questions

1.01

1 kilogram (kg)

2 metre (m)

3 second (s)

4 $\times 1000$; $\times \frac{1}{1000}$; $\times \frac{1}{1\,000\,000}$

5 **a** 1600 g **b** 1.3 m

6 1st row - metre; 2nd row - Mass, kg;
3rd row - second, s

7 gram, millimetre, milligram, tonne, millisecond, micrometre

8 **a** 1000 **b** 10 **c** 100 **d** 100 000 **e** 1 000 000

9 **a** 1000 mm **b** 1500 mm **c** 1534 mm
d 1.652 m

10 **a** 1000 g **b** 1.750 g **c** 26 000 kg **d** 6000 ms

1.02

1 **a** $2000\,cm^3$ **b** 200 ml

2 **a** 2700 kg **b** 27 000 kg

3 **a** $1\,m^3$ of water **b** 1 kg of petrol

4 **a** X **b** Y **c** X

5 X - steel, Y - aluminium

2.01

1 **a** current **b** conductor **c** insulator

2 **a** copper **b** PVC

3 **a** cell **b** generator

4 **a** torch, portable radio
b any two mains appliances

5 **a** electric drill, food mixer **b** iron, toaster
c telephone, radio

2.02

1 cell, complete circuit

2 **a** cell **b** switch **c** bulb

3 **a** ammeters **b** same **c** go out **d** go out
e zero **f** zero 4

2.03

2 voltmeter

3 voltage

4 **a** battery **b** bulbs **c** 2 V **d** 3 V
e X 8 V, Y 4 V, Z 4 V

5 4 V

2.04

1 ohm (Ω)

2 resistance = voltage/current

3 **a** resistance can be varied
b bulb brighter; less resistance in circuit

4 more resistance

5 A 4 Ω, B 1.5 Ω, C 0.4 Ω

2.05

1 **a** thermistor **b** diode

2 **a** 1 A **b** 3 A **c** 2 Ω **d** 4 Ω

3 1st row 4 Ω, 2nd row 1 A,

4 Ω, 3rd row 0.5 A, 4 Ω

2.06

2 **a** A OFF, B ON **b** A OFF, B OFF

3 **a** 8 V **b** 2 A **c** 4 A

4 **a** 2 V **b** 4 V

2.07

1 12 V

2 A 4 Ω, B 15 V, C 1.5 A, D 0.5 Ω

3 **a** 3 A **b** 1.5 A **c** 4.5 A

2.08

1 230 V

2 alternating current

3 battery gives one-way current (DC)

4 breaks circuit if current too high

5 stops casing ever becoming live

6 **a** live **b** earth **c** live **d** neutral

7 **a** 13 A **b** 3 A **c** fault may not blow fuse

8 **a** wire to bulb live even when switch is off

2.09

1 watt (W)

2 1600 W

3 A (drill) 460 W; B (toaster) 690 W; C (stereo player) 92 W

4 **a** A 0.46 kW, B 1.15 kW, C 0.92 kW, D 0.023 kW
    b A 2A, B 5A, C 4A, D 0.1A
    c A 3A, B 13A, C 13A, D 3A

2.10

1 full voltage across each, independently switched
2 fuses (or circuit breakers)
3 **a** breaks circuit if current is too high
    b can be reset
5 AC backwards and forwards, DC one way
6 current goes backwards and fowards 50 times a second

2.11

1 **a** watt, joule, kilowatt-hour   **b** J, kWh
2 2 seconds
3 switched on for less time
4 **a** 15 kWh   **b** £1.50 (150p)   **c** 0.1 kW
    d 1.2 kWh   **e** 12p 5 Dan

2.12

1 plus (+), minus (-)
2 taken from atoms in hair
3 **a** attract   **b** repel   **c** attract
4 **a** electrons taken from atoms in sleeve
    b attracted charges closer than repelled ones

2.13

1 **a** sparks when aircraft refuelled   **b** earthing
2 **a** pushed down   **b** inkjet printer   **c** pulled up
3 charged atoms (or groups of atoms)
4 contains ions

3.01

1 5 m/s
2 velocity has direction
3 speed changes by 4 m/s every second
4 12 m/s
5 4 s
6 from 4 s to 9 s
7 9 m/s
8 3 m/s^2
9 9 s
10 2 m/s^2

3.02

1 **a** D   **b** B   **c** A

3.03

1 **a** accelerating   **b** steady speed
    c decelerating (retarding)   **d** 30 m/s   **e** 25 s
    f 30 m/s   **g** 3 m/s^2
2 **a** stopped•   **b** AB   **c** BC   **d** 40 m, 10 s   **e** 4 m/s

3.04

1 kilogram, newton
2 **a** kg   **b** N   **c** N
3 tension, weight, air resistance
4 20 N, 40 N, 5 N

3.05

1 wheel bearings
2 tyre, to stop skidding
3 **a** tyre, brake pad   **b** shaft
    c roller bearings, grease
    d prevent wear and overheating
4 streamlined wheels, frame, helmet
5 **a** streamlining, less speed
    b less fuel used, less noise

3.06

1 C and D
2 **a** terminal speed   **b** air resistance   **c** equal
    d reduced, bigger 'chute means less speed for same air resistance

3.07

1 **b** 6 N   **c** downwards
2 **a** right   **b** gain speed   **c** less acceleration
    d more acceleration
3 **a** left   **b** lose speed; resultant opposes motion
    c steady speed

3.08

2 driver tired, affected by alcohol
3 airbags, seat belts, crumple zone
4 B, C, D
5 **a** 15 m   **b** 18 m
6 50 m

3.09

1 **b** 500 N
2 equal but opposite force on gun
3 force has almost no effect on massive Earth

3.10

3 **a** Y; force X distance greater
  b move Y further from nut
4 **a** 200 N m **b** 200 N m **c** 0.5 m
5 in the middle

3.11

1 larger area, so less pressure
2 3 Pa
3 **a** 100 Pa **b** 50 Pa
4 **a** 200 Pa **b** 100 N **c** greater

3.12

1 elastic material returns to original shape after stretching force removed
2 **c** straight line **d** up to 3 N **e** 2.3 N
3 **b** pressure rises as volume decreased **c** 33 cm^3
4 12m^3

4.01

1 **a** longitudinal - backwards-forwards vibrations, transverse - side-to-side vibrations **b** transverse
2 1st row 32 m/s; 2nd row 32 m/s, 2 m; 3rd row 32 m/s, 32 Hz
3 **a** B b B c A
4 **a** 20 mm **b** 12 mm

4.02

1 **a** reflection **b** refraction **c** and **d** diffraction
2 **a** reflected **b** refracted **c** diffracted
  d diffracted less

4.03

1 Sun, bulb
2 paper, table
3 **a** aluminium, snow, **b** coal **c** glass, water
4 sunlight reaches Earth
5 solar cells produce electricity
6 shadows, we can't see round corners
7 **a** 300 000 km/s **b** more than 1 s

4.04

1 **a** angle of incidence **b** 60º
2 **a** diffraction through net curtain b holes in net very small, so wavelength must be very small for diffraction to occur

4.05

1 refraction
2 and **5** because of refraction
3 **b** reflected back in same direction
4 **a** spectrum **b** violet **c** red

4.06

2 because of total internal reflection
3 **a** carrying telephone signals, endoscope
  b rear reflector
4 for internal reflection above this angle, there is no refracted ray

4.07

1 same speed, travel through empty space
2 **a** light
  b X-rays, gamma rays
  c radio waves
  d microwaves
  e infrared
  f light
  g infrared, microwaves
  h ultraviolet
  i X-rays, gamma rays
  j infrared
  k radio waves, microwaves, light, infrared
  l ultraviolet

4.08

1 analogue varies continuously, digital pulses represent numbers
2 make signals larger
3 **a** pulses of light or infrared
  b better quality, can carry more lots of information
  c carry more signals, less power loss
  d long waves diffract more than VHF
5 **a** frequency modulation, amplitude modulation
6 **a** 2 000 000 **b** 2 000 000 Hz **c** 2000 k Hz

4.09

1 wavelength
2 longitudinal, not transverse
3 **a** vibrations b compressions
4 **a** people can hear in air
  b people can hear underwater
  c sounds travel through walls
4 can't hear bell in jar when air removed

5 **a** no material to vibrate **b** sound diffracted
6 oscilloscope shows graph, not waves

4.10
1 sound much slower than light
2 refraction
3 jet plane
4 1320 m
5 **a** warm air **b** solid
6 **a** 660 m **b** 2 s

4.11
1 A higher pitch than B
2 **a** Z **b** Z **c** Y **d** Y
3 B
4 0.5 m

4.12
1 sound with higher frequency than human ear can hear
2 measuring depth of water
4 **a** safer for baby and mother
  b breaking up kidney stones
5 cleaning, testing for flaws in metals
6 **a** 40 000 Hz **b** 140 m **c** 70 m

4.13
1 earthquakes
2 seismograph
3 **a** Z **b** X **c** Y **d** Y **e** Z **f** Z **g** X

4.14
1 jigsaw fit of continents
2 rock and fossil patterns, sea-floor spreading
3 huge pieces of crust (and upper mantle)
4 **a** plate boundaries
  b crust weak and cracked at plate boundaries
5 convection currents in mantle

4.15
1 molten rock
2 **a** and **b** towards each other
  c past each other
3 heating effect of friction
4 rocks heated
5 crystal size

5.01
1 1 day
2 1 year
3 **a** night **b** night **c** daytime
4 reflects sunlight
5 planet appears to move relative to stars

5.02
1 and **2** Mercury, Venus, Mars, Pluto
3 Mercury
4 **a** Mars, Jupiter, Saturn, Uranus, Neptune, Pluto
  b further from Sun
5 **a** gravity
  b Venus
  c Earth
  d reflects sunlight
  e hotter than Mercury, but further from Sun

5.03
1 Venus
2 pieces of rock and ice
3 elliptical orbit takes it further out
4 no solid surface
5 meteor is flash of light, meteorite reaches ground
6 **a** X **b** X **c** Z **d** dust and gas stream off
  e reflects sunlight

5.04
1 **a** travels over whole of Earth's surface
  b to keep speed
  c communications, navigation, research
2 **a** go out into space **b** fall back to Earth
3 geostationary orbit, so satellite orbits at same rate as Earth turns
4 **a** A **b** B

5.05
1 and **2** hydrogen
3 **a** star system
  b our galaxy
  c all the galaxies, everything
  d distance travelled by light in 1 year
4 no; at different distances from Earth
5 **a** 300 000 km **b** 100 billion **c** 100 000 light years
  d 100 **e** 8 minutes **f** 4 light years
  g 9 million million km **h** 36 million million km

5.06

1 **a** huge cloud of gas and dust   **b** gravity
   c 4500 million years   **d** planets and moons
2 **a** core   **b** hydrogen   **c** 6000 million years
3 **a** huge red star   **b** core will become white dwarf
4 **a** gigantic explosion of massive star
   b neutron star

5.07

1 light showed galaxies rushing away
2 galaxies rushing apart, radio 'echo'
3 more than 10 billion years
4 from radio waves
5 **a** gravity   **b** expansion speeding up

6.01

1 joule (J)
2 80 J
3 160 J
4 joule (J)
5 petrol, food
6 **a** kinetic   **b** 300 kJ   **c** 6000 J

6.02

2 changed into heat
3 **a** toaster   **b** pole vaulter   **c** sprinter
4 kinetic → heat
5 energy changed into other forms
6 10 N
7 **a** 40 N   **b** 240 J   **c** 240 J   **d** 240 J
   e changed into heat

6.03

1 **a** 120 J   **b** 240 J
2 **a** 120 J   **b** 120 J
3 **a** 8 J   **b** 32 J
4 four times the KE to lose, so much greater braking distance

6.04

1 metals
2 air trapped in them
3 **a** bottom must conduct, handle must insulate
   b trapped air   **c** water better conductor than air

4 **a** and **b** because of convection
   c hot water rises by convection
5 insulation in attic, walls; air in double glazing

6.05

1 **a** and **b** matt black   **c** silvery
2 **a** absorb Sun's radiation   **b** carry heat away
   c silvery walls
4 **a** white reflects Sun's radiation
   b black better absorber of radiation
   c shiny surface poor emitter of radiation

6.06

1 useful energy output half of energy input
2 transforms twice as much energy per second
3 **a** 0.4 (40%)   **b** wasted as heat
4 200 W 5   **a** 3000 W   **b** 3000 J   **c** 0.75 (75%)
6 **a** 6000 J   **b** 300 J   **c** 300 W
7 other 85% of energy becomes heat

6.07

1 coal, oil, natural gas, nuclear fuel
2 nuclear
3 **a** boiler
   b turning turbines c turbines d condense steam
4 **a** in turbines
   b heat
   c X 2000 MW, Y 500 MW
   e X

6.08

1 hydroelectric, tidal, wind farm
2 global warming
3 by water rushing from behind dam
4 generator turned by wind turbine
5 **a** acid rain   **b** fitting FGD units
6 **a** no carbon dioxide emitted
   b waste radioactive, leaked gas and dust spreads easily

6.09

1 can't be replaced; oil, coal
2 hydroelectric, wind farm
3 Sun → plants → oil → petrol
4 fuel made from plant or animal matter
5 non-renewable, global warming

6 a Middle East **b** natural gas
  c North America, Europe

7.01

1 north-seeking, south-seeking
2 a and **b** S-pole
3 using compass
4 a N-poles at top, S-poles at bottom
  b apart, S-poles repel
  c steel stays magnetized, iron doesn't

7.02

1 a higher current, more turns   **b** reverse current
  c put steel rod in coil, pass current through coil

7.03

1 loses magnetism when current through coil switched off
2 higher current, more turns
3 reverse current
4 a smaller current through switch
  b electromagnet closes contacts to complete output circuit
5 a break circuit if current too high
  b can be reset
  c break circuit at lower current

7.04

1 a greater force   **b** force reversed
2 a higher current, stronger magnet
  b reverse current, reverse magnet
3 every time current reverses, force reverses
4 a stronger turning effect   **b** turning effect reversed

7.05

1 a brushes b commutator
2 a currents are in opposite directions
  b higher current, stronger magnet
  c reverse current, reverse magnet
3 will work on AC

7.06

1 a current reversed   **b** no current
2 a and **b** higher current   **c** no current
3 a higher current   **b** current reversed
  c higher current

7.07

1 generate AC
2 higher voltage (and current)
3 a alternating current, direct current   **b** AC c AC
4 a increase AC voltage   **b** decrease AC voltage
5 a connect rotating coil to outside circuit
  b higher voltage (and current), higher frequency AC
  c fixed coil, rotating magnet
  d to change AC to DC

7.08

1 a generation   **b** transmission
2 a national supply network
  b high demand can be met by power stations outside area
3 stepping voltage up or down
4 to reduce current in cables
5 stepping down voltage, distributing power
6 transformers only work with AC
7 in area of outstanding natural beauty

8.01

1 a electrons   **b** neutrons   **c** electrons
2 a and **b** 13   **c** 14
3 different number of neutrons in nucleus
4 a $^{12}_{6}C$ **b** $^{16}_{8}O$ **c** $^{226}_{88}Ra$
5 X carbon, Y carbon, Z nitrogen

8.02

1 carbon-14
2 alpha, beta, gamma
3 detecting alpha, beta, gamma
4 creates ions (makes atoms gain or lose electrons)
5 a gamma   **b** alpha   **c** beta   **d** gamma
  e alpha   **f** gamma   **g** alpha

8.03

1 radon gas from ground
2 radon is radioactive
3 a alpha   **b** can't penetrate skin
4 a 2 counts per second   **b** 26 counts per second
  c gamma

8.04

1 strontium-90

Answers

2 a 400 Bq **b** 200 Bq **c** 50 Bq

3 a decay happens at random **b** 1.5 hours

8.05

1 a radioactive isotopes
  b in nuclear reactors c tracers, radiotherapy

2 radiotherapy, testing metals for cracks

3 a alpha completely stopped, gamma not stopped at all
  b less beta detected

4 a small amount of radioactive material that can be tracked
  b checking thyroid function
  c almost no radiation left after a few days

5 remains can be dated

End of chapter questions

Chapter 1 Units and measuring (p14)

1 metre m, kilogram kg, time second, current A, celsius or kelvin °C or K, m^2, volume, force N.

2 a 1000 **b** 1000 **c** 1 000 000 **d** 4 000 000
  e 500 000

3 a 3 m **b** 0.5 kg **c** 1.5 km **d** 0.25 s **e** 500 ms
  f 750 m **g** 2500 **h** 800 mm

4 24 cm^3, 4 cm, 10 cm, 5 cm

5 a 8 g/cm^3 **b** 9 g/cm^3 **c** 19 g/cm^3

6 a 10.8 g **b** 16.0 g **c** 200 g

7 a 5 cm^3 **b** 2 cm^3 **c** 9 cm^3

Chapter 2 Electricity (p48-51)

1 a Yes, No, No, Yes, Yes **b** conductor, insulator

4 a C **b** B

5 a 6 Ω **b** 0.5 A

6 i parallel **ii** 4 A **iii** 2 A **iv** no effect

7 i series **ii** 3 V **iii** goes out

8 i a all out **b** just one out **ii a** Family B
  b 40 V 240 V **c** 0.25 A 0.33 A **d** No

9 a 2 A **b** 12 W

10 i 0.2 Wh **ii** 2.4 p

11 a 0.1 kW, 0.02 kW **b** 20 kWh **c** 100 kWh
  d £8 **e** heat

12 i neutral blue, yellow/green, live brown
  ii earth – safety **iii** earth wire

13 cable grip, incorrect pin for brown, loose earth wire

14 a i S$_1$ **ii** S$_1$ and S$_2$ **b** 8.5 A **c** 13 A **d** Y
  e safety **f** blue **g** brown
  h ii double insulation

15 i electrical energy to heat and light energy **ii** 2 kW
  iii casing **iv** live wire **v** 8.6 A **vi** 13 A
  vii too large a current **viii** turn it off

Chapter 3 Forces and motion (p82-85)

1 a acceleration, constant speed, slowing down, stopped, acceleration, court speed

2 a Jane **b** Emma **c** 5 s **d** 7 m/s

3 a 2 m/s **b** 5 m/s **c** 0 m/s **d** 2 m/s

4 a reaction time, weather

5 a between feet and ice, between ice and bobsleigh
  b streamline themselves **c** stopping

6 a high **b** high **c** high **d** low **e** high
  f low

7 i gravity; increases **i** Newtons **ii** gravitational potential; kinetic **b** 2000 J or 2 kJ

8 a lead ball **b** air resistance for braking

9 a 10 km/h/s **b** 4 km/h/s, –4 km/h/s **c** 10 m/s^2

10 a 10 **c** 3 s **d i** gravity **ii** air resistance
  iii downword **iv** equal **e** lower terminal velocity

11 c 200 Nm **d** 200 Nm **e** 0.5 m **f** at end
  g 200 N

12 a 200 000 Pa **b** 50 000 Pa **c** 6000 Pa

13 a 1 N/mm^2 **b** 500 N/mm^2

15 a 12 mm **b** proportional **c i** 6 mm **ii** 9 mm
  d permanently stretched

Chapter 4 Rays and waves (p122-125)

1 b i C **ii** B

2 A

3 b changes direction

5 b total internal reflection **c** binoculars

8 E

9 a quicker return of echo **b** sunken wreck
  c i 750 m **ii** $\frac{1}{3}$ s

10 a B louder **b** C higher pitch **c** B **d** C
  e 1.5 m **f** 440 Hz

11 a P is quieter and lower pitched than Q

12 a reflection of sound **c** 340 m/s
  d high frequency sounds we can't hear
  e scanning unborn baby

13 a i 20 kHz **ii** Y **b i** scanning unborn babies
  ii less dangerous **iii** cleaning

14 a infra red **b** X-rays **c i** gamma **ii** radio
  iii radio **iv** ultra violet **v** microwaves
  vi infra red **vii** ultraviolet **viii** visible light
  d i red **ii** violet

15 b i higher pitch **ii** louder

16 d 40 Hz

17 light, ultraviolet, gamma rays, microwaves,
radioactive materials

18 a infra red **b** better absorber

Chapter 5 The Earth in Space (p144-145)

1 a star **b** satellite **c** constellation **d** galaxy

2 a receiving sunlight **b** not receiving sunlight
  c 1 day **d** moon **e** gravitational forces
  f larger

3 a suns/stars **b** moon **c i** moving across stars
  ii object orbiting **d i** planet **ii** weather satellite

4 a B **b** B **c** A **d** above same place on Earth
  e constant contact

5 a 12

6 a Jupiter **b** Pluto **c** Mercury **d** Jupiter
  e 0.2 years **f** hotter closer to Sun

7 a Venus **b** Jupiter **c** Smaller gravitational force
from Sun **d** Between Mars and Jupiter **e** 6 or 7
years **f** ellipse

8 a moon **b** Solar system **c** meteorite **d** comet
  e galaxy **f** super nova

Chapter 6 Energy (p172-175)

1 a C **b** B **c** D **d** A

2 a 60 000 J **b** 200 W **c** friction, noise

3 a 500 N **b** 10 000 J **c** electrical to gravitational
potential **d** 1000 W or 1 kW **e** 20 000 J
  f friction, weight of bucket **g** lighter bucket,
lubrication

4 a i non polluting **ii** intermittent energy
  iii noise, unsightly

5 a kinetic energy **b** friction, heat

6 a can be replaced **b** rainwater **c** non polluting
  d flooding

7 a 40 000 **b i** 1 MJ **ii** 2 MJ all potential energy
is converted to kinetic energy **c** 1.2 MJ **d** less
demand

8 a i chemical **ii** kinetic **iii** gravitational
potential **b** heat

9 a sunlight **b i** heat **ii** 80%

10 a network of wires carry electrical energy **b i** oil

ii find new sources, reduce oil usage

11 a i coal, gas **ii** coal **iii** gas **iv** never used up
  b i intermittent **ii** unsightly

12 a good absorber **b** prevent heat loss
  c convection current **d** more sunlight **e** 2 kW
  f 5 m^2 **g** non-polluting, intermittent

14 a 'water jacket' fibreglass/foam **b** heats whole
tank **c i** 1000 **ii** 3000 J **iii** 1 200 000

15 double glazing, loft insulation, cavity wall insulation,
carpets and underlay, draft excluders

16 a & b Convection **c** Condensation
  d Convection

Chapter 7 Magnets and currents (p198-199)

1 a nails fall **b** do not fall **c** more current or turns
  d electric bell, relay switch

4 a A to B **b** moves to the right
  c moves to the left

5 a i stronger magnet **ii** more loops of wire
  iii faster rotation

6 a generators, coal, oil, gas. Chemical energy →
electrical energy **b** less energy loss **c** safety
  d voltage decrease, step down transformer
  e change voltage using transformers
  f 12 V stepdown

7 a stepdown **b** 800 turns

Chapter 8 Atoms and nuclei (p214-215)

1 a negative **b** proton **c** positive **d** 4
  e electrons

2 a 7 positive, 7 neutral, 7 negative **b** same element
but differing numbers of neutrons

3 a 2 protons joined with 2 neutrons **b** electron
  c electromagnetic wave **d** nucleus
  e Geiger-Müller tube **f** card **g** lead

4 a α and β radiation **b** lead stops all types of
radiation

5 a rocks, e.g. granite, nuclear power stations

6 a electrons **b** Geiger-Müller tube **c** smaller
  d α unable to pass through paper, γ count unaffected
by paper thickness

7 a Increase count rate, high concentration of
radioactive material **b** γ, high penetration, power
needed

8 a 1 billion **b** 5.6 billion **c** 4.6 billion
  d alpha particle **e** fast moving electrons
  f quality control for paper

Answers

9 a α particle **b** nucleus **c** time for half the sample to decay **d i** 400 counts per second **ii** 100 counts per second

Exam-style Questions

1 c 80 km/h

2 a air resistance **b** balanced forces **c** opens parachute **d** deceleration **e** lower terminal velocity

3 a electric fire **b** battery **c** solar cell **d** microphone **e** speaker **f** candle

4 a can't be replaced, can be replaced **b** oil, gas **c** tidal **d** non polluting expensive initial costs

5 a 0.4 A

6 a 24 W **b** 240 J **c** electrical to heat and light

7 a 3 A **b** 3 A **c** 5 A **d** 13 A **e** melts

8 a neutral **b** live **c** yellow/green **d** safety **e** fuse

9 a i £1.26 **ii** 4.2p **iii** 7p **b** a network of pylons and cables carrying electrical energy from power stations to homes

10 a ammeter **b** 2 A **c** 4 A **d** 6 A

11 a variable resistor **b** switch **c** ammeter **d** voltmeter **f** 6/0.80 **g** 8 ohms

12 a electrical energy to heat and light energy **b** 36 J/s **c** 3 A **d** 4 Ω

13 a 12 km **b** 40 minutes **c** 24 h **d** slower, less steep graph

14 a 200 Nm **b** longer spanner

15 a 5 **b** 2 Hz **c** 10 cm/s

16 a gravitational potential energy **b** 15 000 J **c** friction **d** 750 W

17 b 6.0 cm **d** 175 N **e** 75 N

18 a 12 V **b** 4 Ω **c** 2 A **d** 8 V **e** 4 V

19 a pointer 10 divisions to left **b** no pointer movement **c** pointer more than 10 divisions to left **d** magnetic field cutting through coils

20 a heat flows from hot to cold **b** conduction **c** convection **d** cavity wall insulation, e.g. fibreglass

21 a burning fuel **c** cannot be replaced **d** wood **e** increases carbon dioxide in atmosphere

22 a 40% **b** heat warms water produces steam drives turbines and generators **c** National grid

23 a total internal reflection **b** endoscope

24 a return to original shape **b** some permanent deformation **c** 10 cm

25 a midday **b** middle of night **c** dawn **d** sunset **e** 1 day

26 a galaxy **b** planet, comet **c** moon, satellite **d** constellation **e** Sun

27 a A – β, B – α, C – γ **b** α and β **c** α **d** Geiger-Müller tube

28 a elastic, spring, battery **b** kinetic energy **c** can be replaced

29 a electrical, heat, kinetic **b** 1 Unit **c** 9p

30 a C **b** microwaves, infra red **c** radio waves **d** visible light **e** skin cancer **f** avoid exposure, e.g. wear hats, sun creams **g** radioactive materials

31 a friction between runners and ice **b** wear surface, heating

32 b total internal reflection **c** 90°, 180° **d** prismatic periscope

Index

Index